Practice Book: Units 1–4

NATIONAL GEOGRAPHIC

Reach for Reading

COMMON CORE PROGRAM

NATIONAL GEOGRAPHIC LEARNING | CENGAGE Learning

NATIONAL GEOGRAPHIC LEARNING | CENGAGE Learning

Acknowledgments
Grateful acknowledgment is given to the authors, artists, photographers, museums, publishers, and agents for permission to reprint copyrighted material. Every effort has been made to secure the appropriate permission. If any omissions have been made or if corrections are required, please contact the Publisher.

Cover illustration: Joel Sotelo

Cover Design and Art Direction: Visual Asylum

Illustration Credits: All PM illustrations by National Geographic Learning.

For product information and technology assistance, contact us at
Customer & Sales Support, 888-915-3276

For permission to use material from this text or product, submit all requests online at **www.cengage.com/permissions**
Further permissions questions can be emailed to
permissionrequest@cengage.com

National Geographic Learning | Cengage Learning
1 Lower Ragsdale Drive
Building 1, Suite 200
Monterey, CA 93940

Cengage Learning is a leading provider of customized learning solutions with office locations around the globe, including Singapore, the United Kingdom, Australia, Mexico, Brazil, and Japan. Locate your local office at **www.cengage.com/global**.

Cengage Learning products are represented in Canada by Nelson Education, Ltd.

Visit National Geographic Learning online at **NGL.Cengage.com**
Visit our corporate website a **www.cengage.com**

Printed in the USA.
Globus Printing, Minster, OH

ISBN: 978-13054-99010 (Practice Book)

ISBN: 978-13056-58714 (Practice Masters)

Printed in the United States of America

Print Number: 15 Print Year: 2023

Contents

Unit 1: Hello, Neighbor!

Unit 2: Staying Alive

Unit 3: Water for Everyone

Unit 4: Lend a Hand

Name ______________________ Date __________

Phonics

Short *a*

Circle the word that names the picture.

1.  cat cot	**2.**  vat van	**3.**  map man
4.  hat ham	**5.** 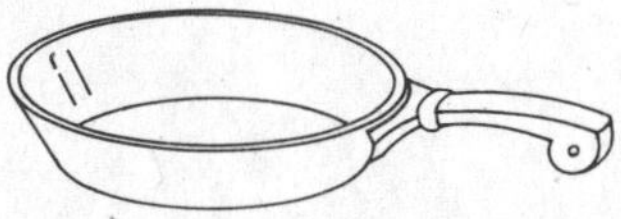 pan pat	**6.**  mad mat
7.  can cab	**8.** 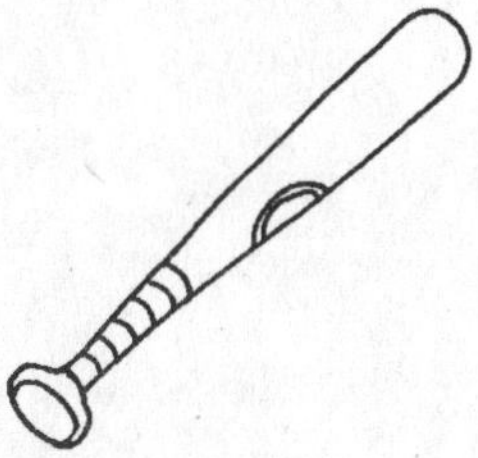 bag bat	**9.**  fat fan

Read It Together Find a hat and a pan.

Name ____________________ Date ____________

Character Map

Character

Make a character map for Jae and Vera from the song "Our Hometown Workers."

Character	Who the Character Is	What the Character's Job Is

Share your character map with a partner.

Name ______________________ Date ____________

Phonics

Short *a*

Write the word that completes each sentence.

1. ran cat

I have a ________ .

2. lap tap

The cat is on my ________ .

3. hat pat

I like to ________ my cat.

4. mat van

Dad is in the ________ .

5. map fat

Dad has a ________ in the van.

6. can bat

The map ________ help him.

7. mat ran

Can you see the ________ ?

8. rat tan

The mat is ________ .

9. sat yam

Jan ________ on the mat.

Name ______________________ Date ____________

Phonics

Final -*s*

Write the word that completes each sentence.

1. pal pals

Dad and Al are __________ .

2. his has

Al __________ a van.

3. is as

Al __________ in the van.

4. cap caps

I see __________ in the van, too.

5. find finds

Al __________ a tan cap!

6. like likes

Dad __________ my tan cap.

7. hat hats

Al and I find a __________ for Dad.

8. is his

It __________ tan.

9. as has

Dad __________ a tan hat, and I have a tan cap!

Name ______________________ Date ______________

Handwriting

High Frequency Words

Trace each High Frequency Word and then write it.

day day

there there

do do

what what

help help

by by

then then

people people

Spelling & Word Work

Word Cards: Words with Short *a*, Final *-s*

 cat	 bat	 ax	 van
maps	ham	man	hat
at	laps	ban	ran
Max	am	traps	dad
tax	mad	slaps	pan
fan	wax	yam	swam
back	caps	flat	sacks

Spelling & Word Work

High Frequency Word Cards

I	see
too	what
have	help
a	people
the	do
my	there
is	by
on	day
it	then

Name ______________________ Date ____________

Phonics

Short *i*

Circle the word that names the picture.

1. 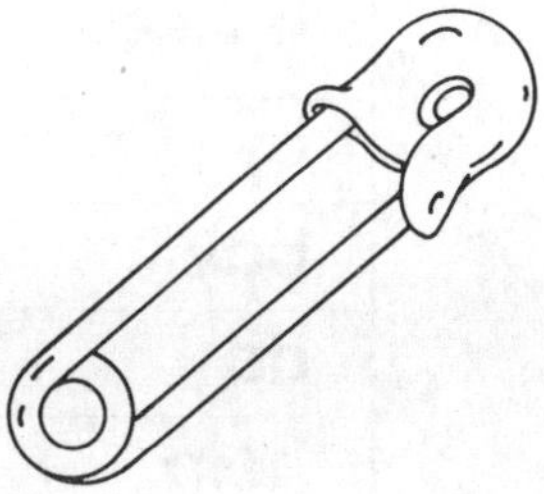 pan pin	**2.**  pig pat	**3.**  cat kid
4.  fin fan	**5.**  wax wig	**6.** 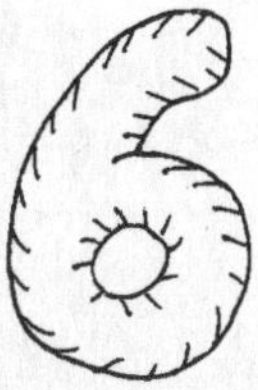 six sat
7. 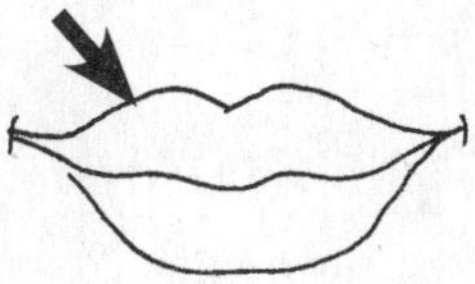 lap lip	**8.**  bib bat	**9.** 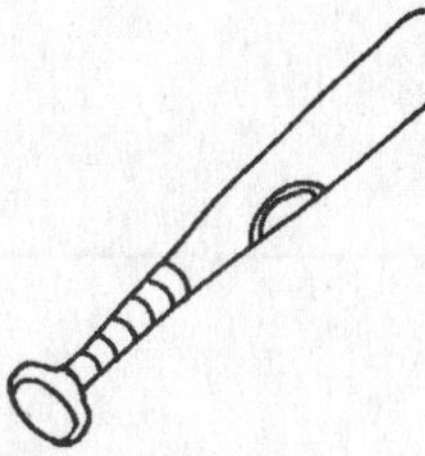 bat bib

Read It Together Where is the pig? Where is the bib?

Name ______________________ Date ______________

High Frequency Words

Max and His Cat

Write a word from the box to complete each sentence.

High Frequency **Words**
by
day
do
help
people
then
there
what

1. Max and his cat have a big ____________ !

2. Max sees his cat go ____________ him.

3. ____________ Max cannot see his cat!

4. Where is his cat? It is up ____________ !

5. ____________ can Max do?

6. He can find ____________ to help!

Grammar: Plural Nouns

Word Cards: Plural Nouns

s	es	y	i + es
box	cat	church	glass
branch	library	lunch	farm
bush	town	park	dish
office	potato	community	place
home	hospital	city	school
store	address	sandwich	road
crash	pony	beach	walk
story	wind	berry	tree

Name ______________________ Date ____________

Phonics

Short *i*

Write the word that completes each sentence.

1. six sax

I have ________ pigs.

2. had hid

That pig ________ by the bin.

3. did dad

I ________ find it there!

4. hit hat

The little pig sat on my tan ________!

5. big bag

This pig is not little. It is ________.

6. pat pit

I like to ________ this pig.

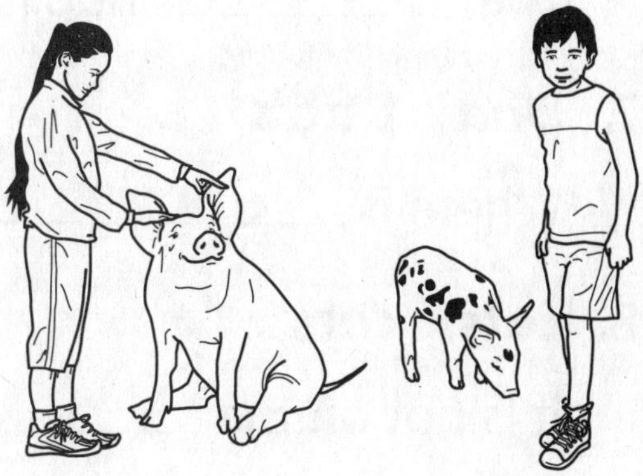

7. It At

________ likes that!

8. as is

That pig ________ not my pig.

9. his has

It is ________ pig!

Name ______________________ Date ____________

Phonics

Possessives

Write the word that completes each sentence.

1. Dan Dan's

This is ____________ cat.

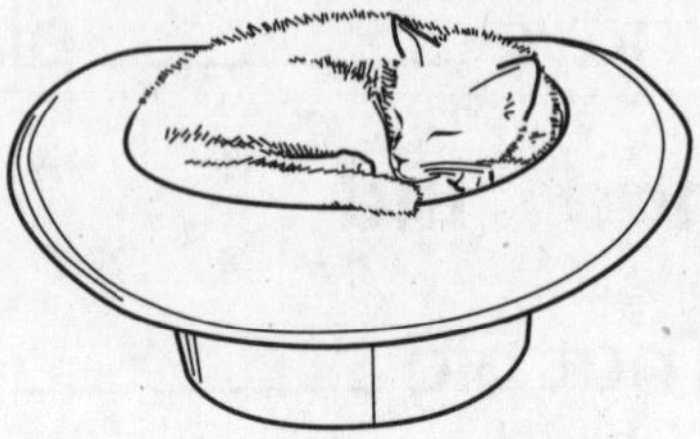

2. Pat Pat's

The cat is in ____________ hat.

3. cat cat's

The ____________ naps in the hat!

4. kids kids'

I see the ____________ cats, too.

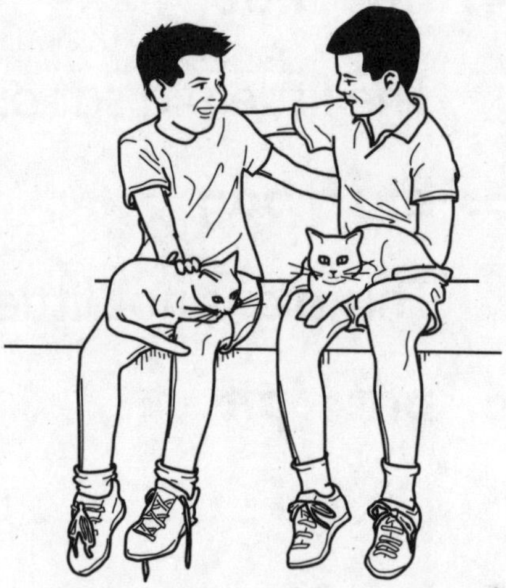

5. pals pals'

The cats are in the ____________ laps.

6. cats cats'

The ____________ nap in the laps.

7. Dad Dad's

Where is ____________ cat?

8. cats cats'

It is not on the ____________ mat.

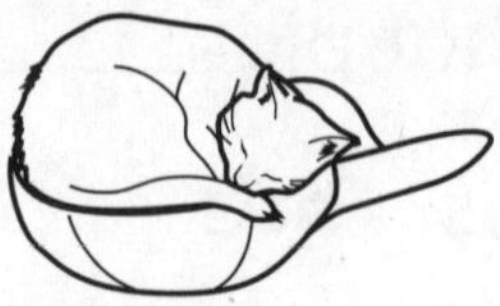

9. Kim Kim's

It naps in ____________ cap!

Name ______________________________ Date ______________

Grammar and Writing

Write Plural Nouns

Read the story. Then choose a word from the box that goes with each sentence and make it plural.

glass	box	party
hat	game	hutch

Last summer, I went to three parties. At one party, we made a big fort out of cardboard ________. We played fun ________ at every party. At Robert's party, we drank apple juice out of cool red ________. At Sarah's party, we got to take her pet rabbits out of their ________. The thing I remember most about Kareem's party is the crazy paper ________ we wore.

Name ______________________________ Date ______________

Character Map

Quinito's Neighborhood

Make a character map for the people in "Quinito's Neighborhood."

Character	Who the Character Is	What the Character's Job Is
Mami and Papi	Quinito's parents	She is a carpenter. He is a nurse.
Guillermo	Quinito's neighbor	
Dona Estrella		She is a seamstress.

Use your character map to describe the characters in "Quinito's Neighborhood" to a partner.

Name ______________________ Date ____________

Phonics

Short *o*

Circle the word that names the picture.

1. 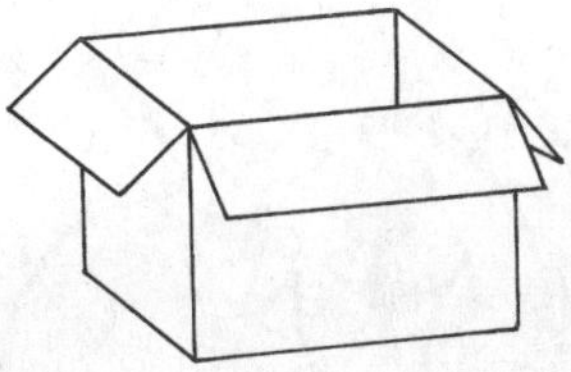 bag box (circled)	**2.**  hot hat	**3.**  lot log
4.  fan fox	**5.** 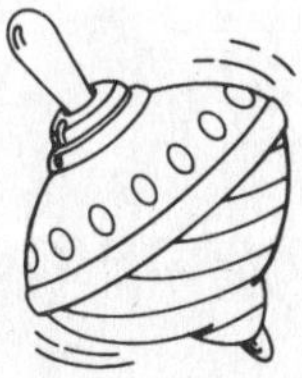 tag top	**6.**  fox fix
7. 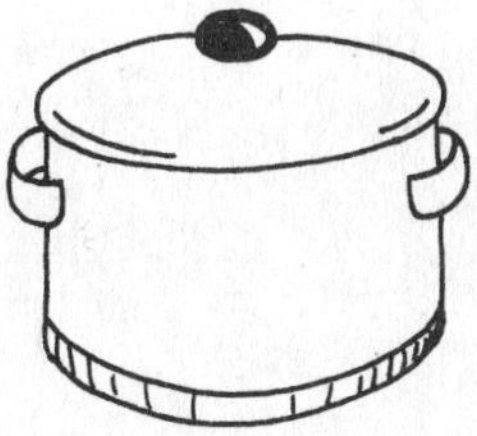 pot pat	**8.** 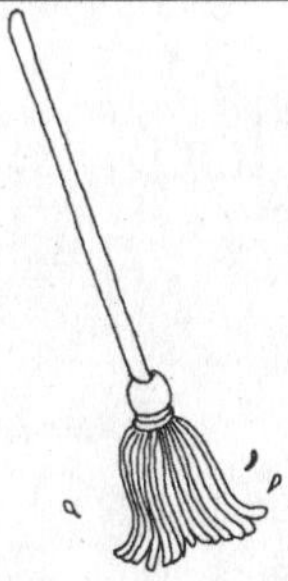 mop man	**9.**  dog dig

Read It Together What can fit in a box?

Name ______________________________ Date ______________

Phonics

Short *o*

Write the word that completes each sentence.

1. dig dog

Jax is my ____________ .

2. big bog

He is ____________ and tan.

3. jig jog

Jax and I like to ____________ .

4. log lag

We see a ____________ by the bog.

5. hat hot

Jax is ____________ .

6. hips hops

Jax ____________ on the log.

7. top tap

He sits on ____________ .

8. fix fox

Look! A ____________ comes out!

9. on an

Jax and I jog ____________ !

Name ______________________ Date ____________

Phonics

Syllables

Circle the word that names the picture.

1.  pit pig	**2.**  cat cot	**3.**  dog dig
4. 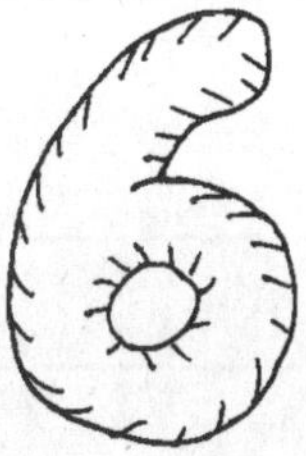 six sax	**5.**  log lot	**6.** 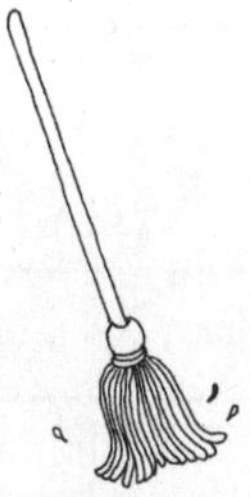 mop map
7.  on ox	**8.**  fan fin	**9.**  wag wig
10. 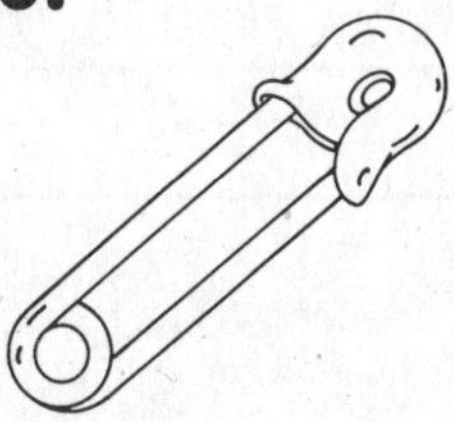 pin pan	**11.**  ax at	**12.**  hot hat

Read It Together A dog can dig. Can you dig, too?

Name ______________________ Date ____________

Handwriting

High Frequency Words

Trace each High Frequency Word and then write it.

come come

from from

her her

look look

of of

one one

out out

some some

Spelling & Word Work

Word Cards: Words with Short *o*

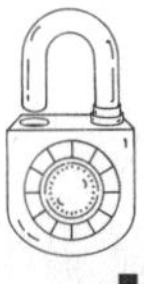 lock	 top	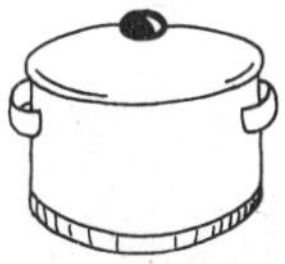 pot	 cob
sob	mop	spot	dot
sock	con	Tom	job
flock	lot	hop	rob
rock	rot	blob	stop
lob	hot	pop	flop
cotton	dock	bottom	Ron

Spelling & Word Work

High Frequency Word Cards

you	are
all	of
not	out
here	one
find	some
his	from
and	come
where	her
little	look

Name ______________________ Date ____________

Comparison Chart

Compare Genres

Show how realistic fiction and a photo-essay are different.

Realistic Fiction	Photo-Essay
• tells about things that could really happen	• uses photographs and text to tell about a topic

Take turns with a partner. Give information about a story or a photo-essay.

Name ______________________ Date ____________

Phonics

Syllable Division

Divide each word into syllables. Circle the word that names the picture.

1. 

bobcat

bobbin

2. 

tidbit

picnic

3. 

rabbit

random

4. 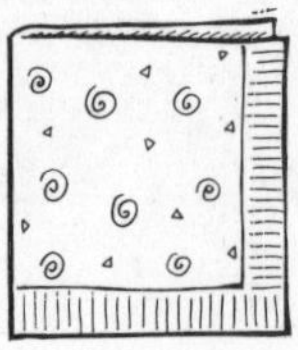

napkin

cannot

5. 

catnap

hatbox

6. 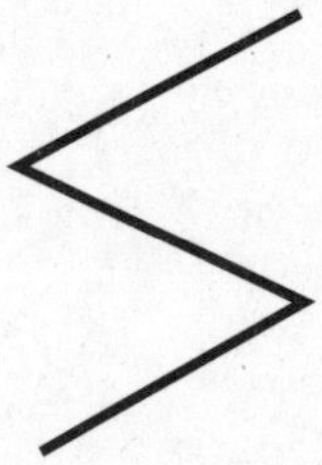

mascot

zigzag

7. 

falcon

fabric

8. 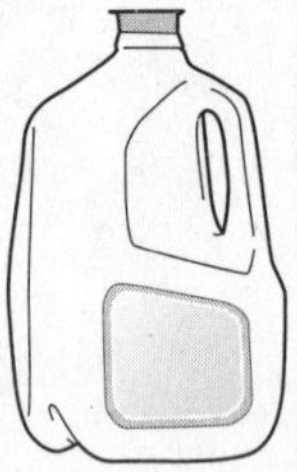

gallon

gossip

9. 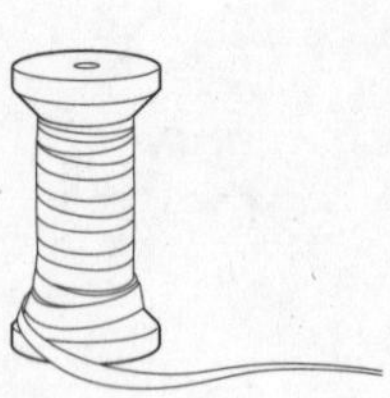

ransom

ribbon

Read It Together Do you see a bobcat or a napkin at a picnic?

Name ______________________ Date ____________

High Frequency Words

Hats in a Box

Write a word from the box to complete each sentence.

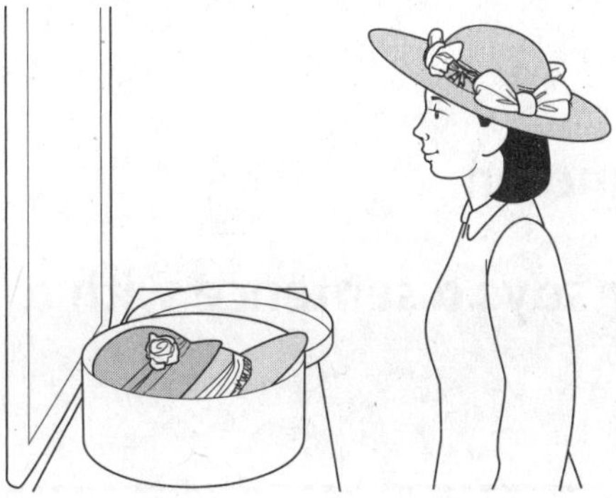

High Frequency **Words**
come
from
her
look
of
one
out
some

1. Jan got this hatbox ____________ her attic.

2. Come ____________ at it.

3. There are ____________ hats in the box!

4. ____________ hat has ribbons.

5. A lot ____________ the ribbons are big!

6. Look! That hat is ____________ of the box and on Jan!

Name ______________________ Date ____________

Grammar: Plural Nouns

Use Plural Nouns

1. Take turns with a partner.

2. Toss a marker onto the game board.

3. Follow the directions in the square you land on.

4. After you say your sentence, your partner says a sentence with a different noun of the same type.

Say a sentence with a plural noun that ends in **s**.	Say a sentence with a plural noun that changes its spelling.
Say a sentence with a plural noun that ends in **es**.	Say a sentence with a plural noun that does not change its form.
Say a sentence with a plural noun that ends in **ies**.	Say a sentence with a collective noun.

Name ______________________________ Date ______________

Phonics

Syllable Division

Divide the words into syllables. Write the word that completes each sentence.

1. picnic gallon

Mom, Dad, Ron, and Ron's dog are on a ______________.

2. canyon catnap

Ron's dog, Sam, had a ______________. Then he got up.

3. cannot bobcat

Sam ______________ sit. He digs!

4. napkin attic

He digs up one ______________.

5. zigzag ribbon

He digs up some ______________.

6. admit fabric

He finds some tan ______________, too.

7. fossil gossip

Look! Sam digs up a ______________!

8. gallon rabbit

It is not from a ______________.

9. tidbit bobcat

It is from a ______________!

Name ____________________ Date ____________

Grammar and Writing

Write Plural and Collective Nouns

Read the story. Then choose a word from the box that goes with each sentence and make it plural if necessary.

lunch	baby	fish
man	family	park

Our neighborhood has two great parks kids can play in. One park has a big pond. You can see lots of moms and dads there pushing their new ________ in strollers. They like to look at the ________ that swim in the pond. One ________ had a picnic on Saturday. The parents and kids ate their ________ sitting under a big maple tree. After they left, two ________ sat under the tree and played guitars.

Name ______________________________ Date ______________

Grammar: Plural Nouns

Say Plural Nouns

1. Play with a partner.
2. Spin the spinner.
3. Change the noun to a plural noun.
4. Say a sentence using the plural noun.

Make a Spinner

1. Put a paper clip in the center of the circle.
2. Hold one end of the paper clip with a pencil.
3. Spin the paper clip around the pencil.

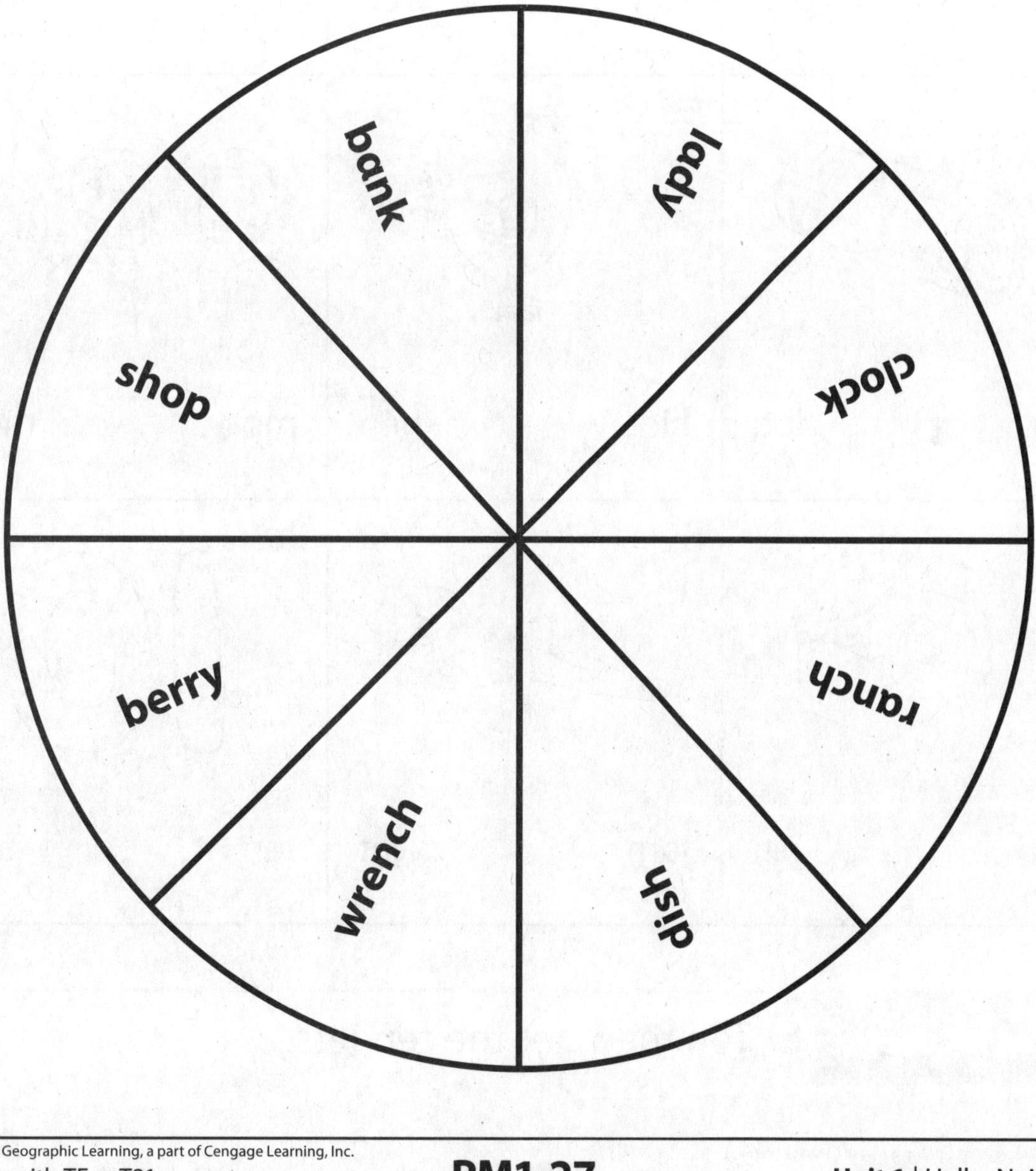

Name ________________________ Date ____________

Phonics

Short e

Circle the word that names the picture.

1. 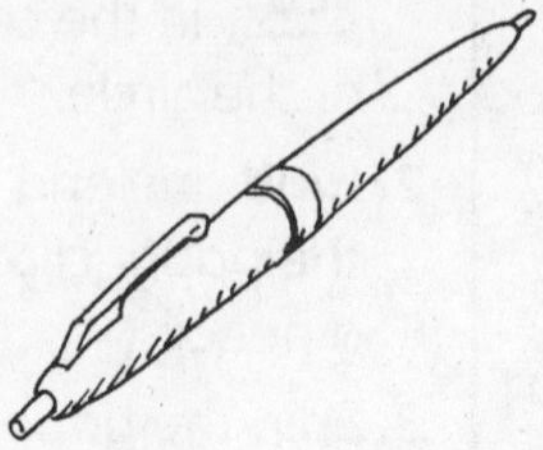 pan pen	**2.** 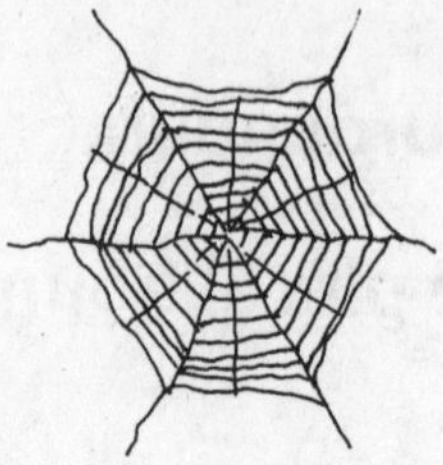 word web	**3.** 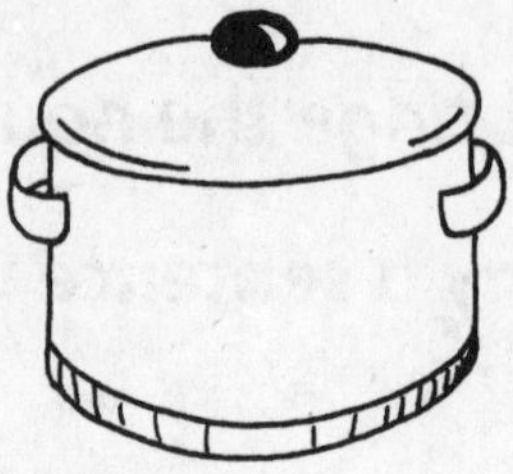 net pot
4.  leg log	**5.**  hid hen	**6.**  mop men
7. 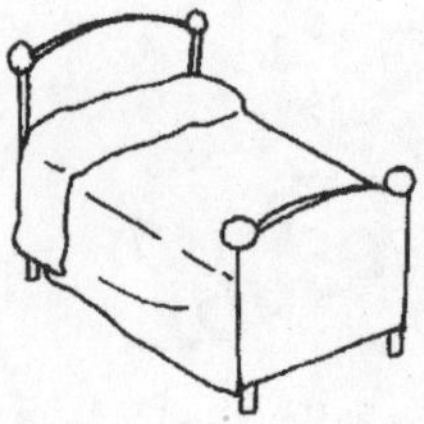 bed bin	**8.**  jam jet	**9.** 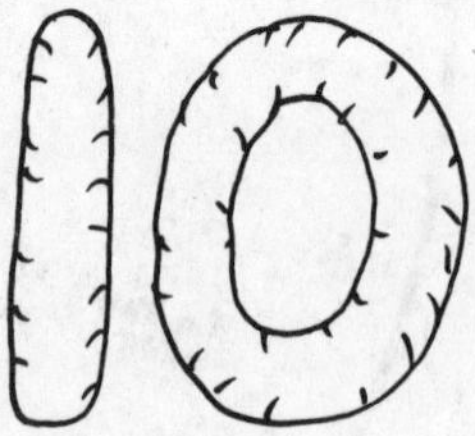 ten tan

Read It Together Ten men get the ten jets.

Name ______________________ Date ____________

Details Cluster

Our Community

Make a details cluster to tell about places in your community.

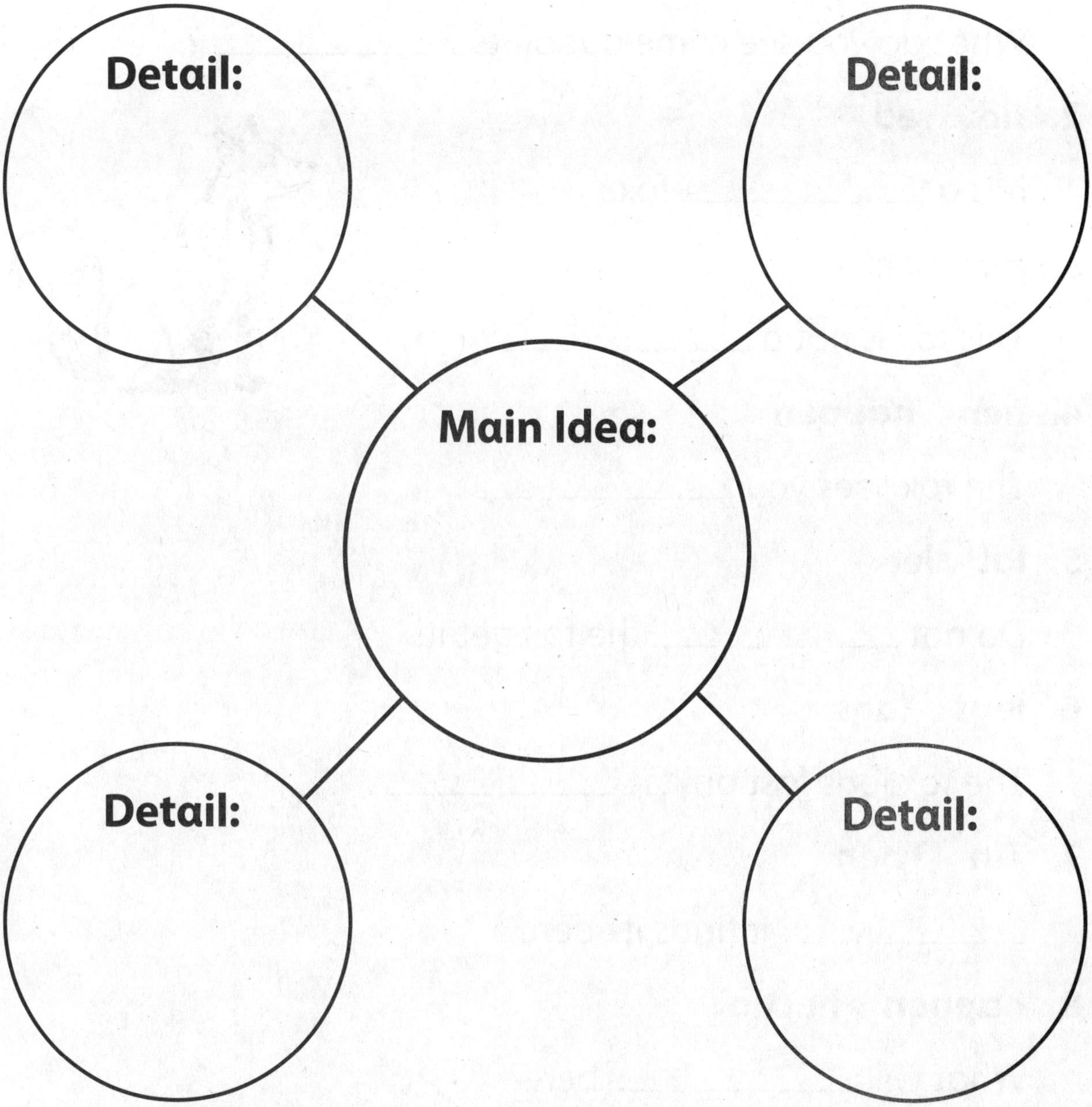

Share your details cluster with a partner. Find out which places you both enjoy in your community.

Name ______________________ Date ____________

Phonics

Short *e*

Write the word that completes each sentence.

1. den din

What do you see come out of its ____________?

2. rid red

It is a ____________ fox.

3. pat pet

This fox is not a ____________.

4. hen happen

The fox sees your ____________.

5. lot let

Do not ____________ the fox get it!

6. legs lags

The fox jogs fast on its ____________.

7. Tin Then

____________ it finds its den.

8. happen hectic

What will ____________ here?

9. bad bed

The fox naps in its ____________!

Name ________________________________ Date ______________

Handwriting

High Frequency Words

Trace each High Frequency Word and then write it.

down down

or or

their their

they they

with with

them them

your your

be be

Spelling & Word Work

Word Cards: Words with short *e*

 jet	 hen	 helmet	 bell
vet	nest	bet	beg
sell	men	peg	pet
tell	best	forget	set
red	help	bell	lend
rest	yell	den	send
ten	fell	test	end

Spelling & Word Work

High Frequency Word Cards

am	as
him	with
for	their
at	be
go	them
to	your
we	down
has	they
she	or

Name ______________________________ Date ______________

Phonics

Short *u*

Circle the word that names the picture.

1.  sun sit	**2.** 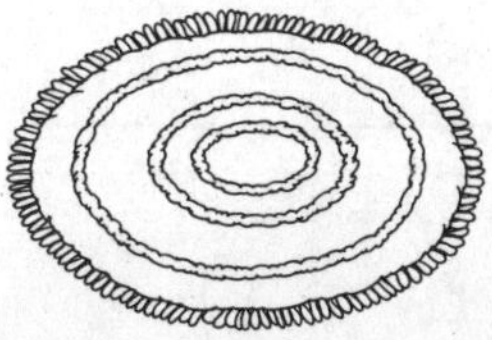 rag rug	**3.** 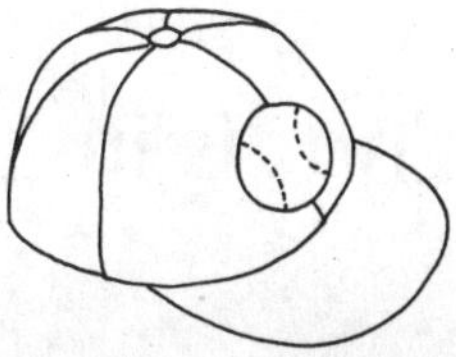 cap cup
4. 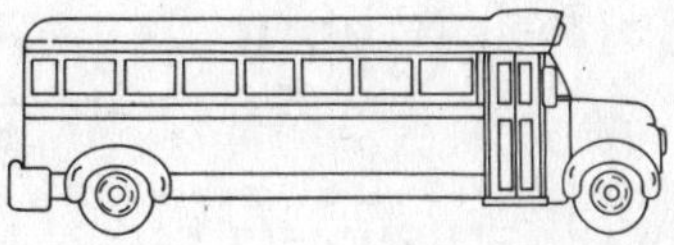 bus bat	**5.**  nut net	**6.** 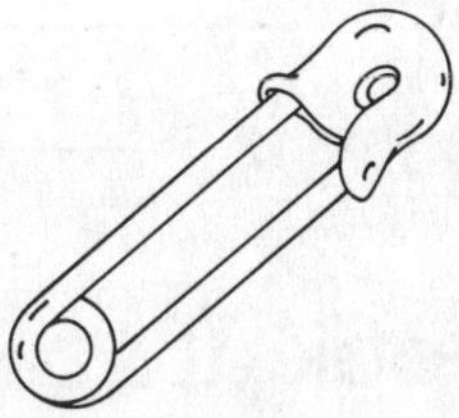 pen pin
7.  big bug	**8.**  tub top	**9.** 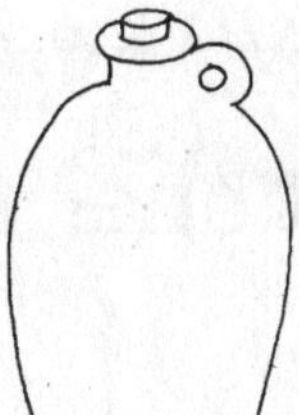 jug job

Read It Together What bugs do you like?

Name ______________________ Date ____________

High Frequency Words

Kittens in a Basket

Write a word from the box to complete each sentence.

High Frequency **Words**
be
down
or
their
them
they
with
your

1. What is in ______________ basket?

2. I have kittens. Look down, and you can see ______________ .

3. Look at ______________ legs. They look like mittens!

4. It can ______________ fun to have a kitten. Can I get one?

5. You can have the big kitten ______________ the little one.

6. You can have fun ______________ your kitten.

Name ______________________ Date ____________

Grammar: Proper Nouns

Use Proper Nouns

1. Take turns with a partner.
2. Toss a marker onto the game board.
3. Follow the directions in the square you land on.

Say a sentence with a **day of the week**.	Say a sentence with a **month**.	Say a sentence with a **holiday**.
Say a sentence with a **day of the week**.	Say a sentence with a **proper noun that names a special date**.	Say a sentence with a **holiday**.
Say a sentence with **two different days of the week**.	Say a sentence with **two different months**.	Say a sentence with **two different holidays**.

Name ______________________________ Date ______________

Phonics

Short *u*

Write the word that completes each sentence.

1. up an

The sun comes ____________, and Gus gets out of bed.

2. mud muffin

He gets a ____________. Yum!

3. nets nuts

It has ____________ in it. Yum! Yum!

4. jogs jugs

Gus ____________ with his pal Jed.

5. us until

They run ____________ ten.

6. hut hot

Then the sun gets too ____________.

7. fun fan

The pals get wet and have ____________.

8. sat sunset

Gus sees the sun go down. He likes the ____________.

9. bed bud

Gus is in his ____________. He had a fun day!

Name ______________________ Date ______________

Grammar and Writing

Write Proper Nouns

Read the story. Then choose a word from the box that goes with each sentence.

September	Fourth of July	Peterson Fireworks Company
Mrs. Minh	Oak Street	Saturday

Brandon was walking down Oak Street. It was a sunny ____________ morning in ____________. Up on the next block he saw lots of flashing lights. *Hmm*, he thought, *it looks like the fireworks on the* ____________. Brandon crossed the street and walked up to the next block. There he saw a bunch of fire engines and police cars. He saw his neighbor ____________ looking at a building. She waved to Brandon and then pointed at ____________________. The building was on fire! *It really is like Independence Day*, thought Brandon.

Name ______________________________ Date ____________

Vocabulary

Vocabulary Bingo

1. Write one Key Word in each building.
2. Listen to the clues. Find the Key Word and use a marker to cover it.
3. Say "Bingo" when you have four markers in a row.

Key Words	
area	locate
building	park
home	place
hospital	population
identify	school
library	

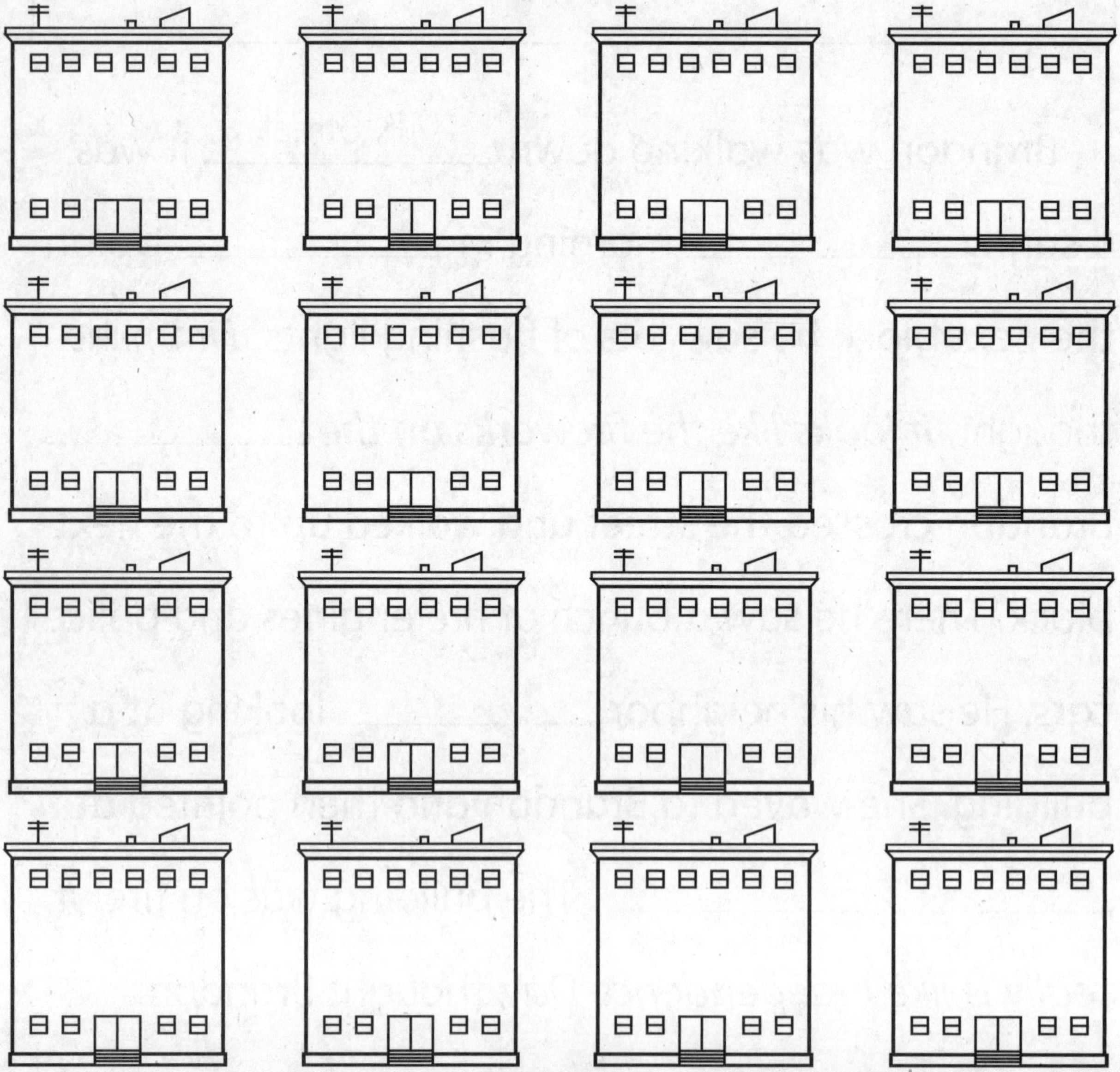

Name ______________________________ Date ______________

Details Cluster

Be My Neighbor

Make a details cluster for "Be My Neighbor." Look for details that tell more about the main idea.

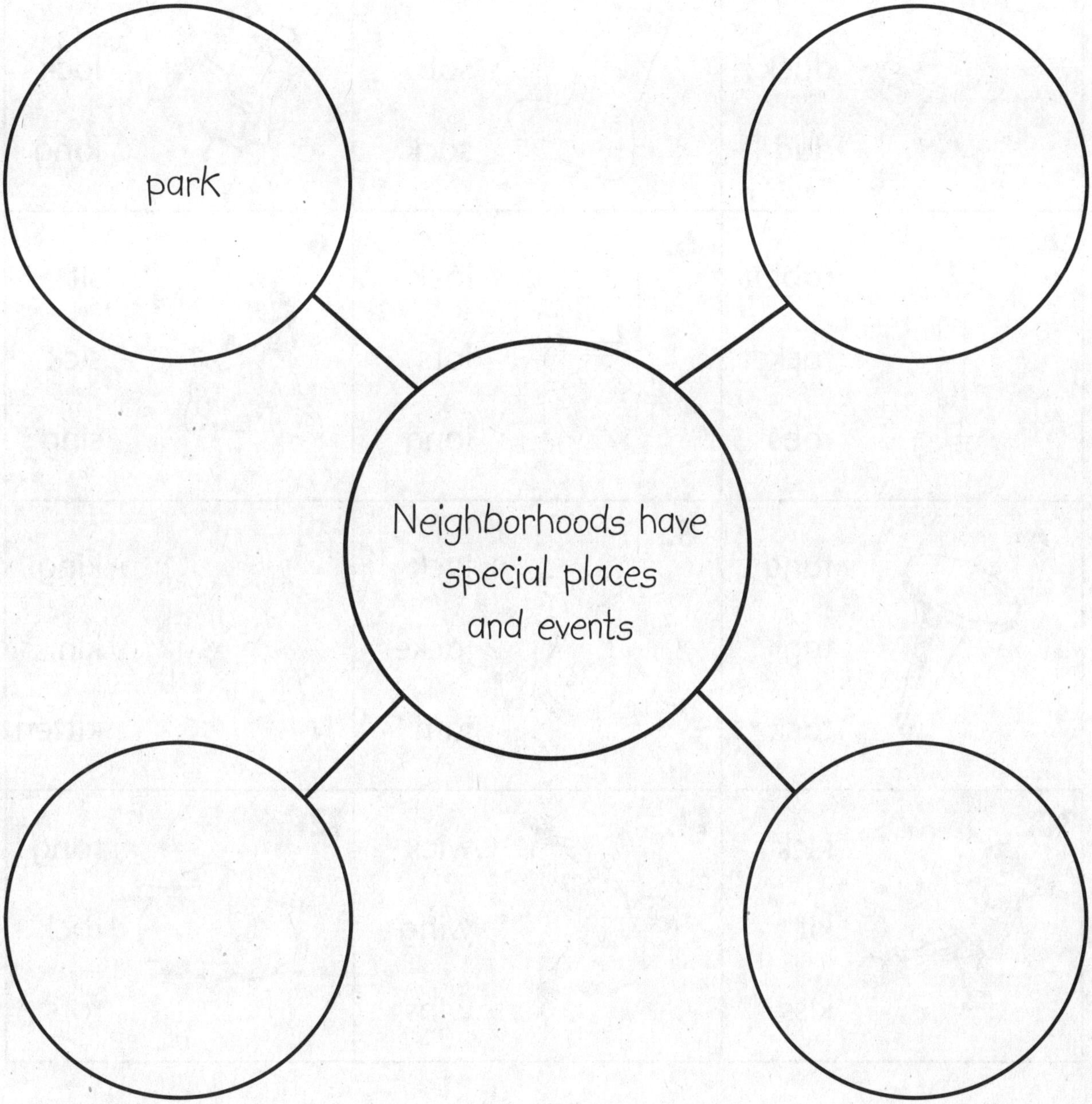

Tell a partner about the main idea and details in "Be My Neighbor."

Name ______________________ Date ____________

Phonics

Consonants *ck, ng*

Circle the word that names the picture.

1. 
dug
duck
dud

2. 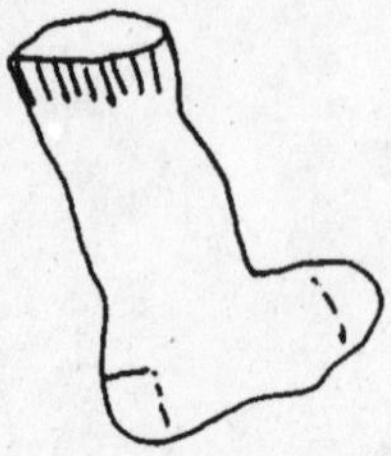
song
sob
sock

3. 
lick
lock
long

4. 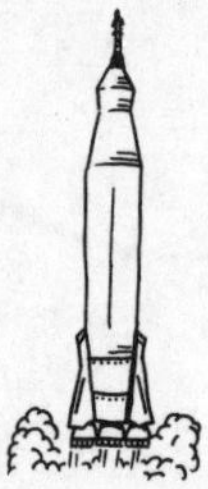
rabbit
rocket
robs

5. 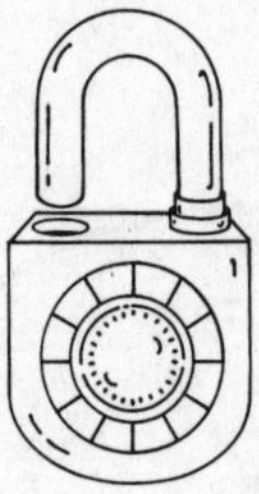
lock
lots
long

6. 
sit
sick
sing

7. 
tang
tag
tack

8. 
jack
jacket
jam

9. 
king
kin
kitten

10. 
kick
kit
kiss

11. 
wick
wing
wins

12. 
rang
rock
rots

Read It Together The king with a ring can sing!

Name ______________________ Date ____________

Phonics

Consonants *ck, ng*

Write the word that completes each sentence.

1. King Kick

_______ Nick is sad.

2. ring rips

He cannot find his red _______ .

3. jogs jacket

He finds his red _______ .

4. people pocket

He looks in the _______ .

5. song sock

He finds a tan _______ with zigzags.

6. pack pang

He finds a _______ of gum, too.

7. dug duck

Then Nick sees his pet _______ .

8. wing wick

The duck has Nick's ring on his _______ .

9. lock long

Nick is not sad! He sings a _______ song!

Name ______________________ Date ____________

Phonics

Double Consonants

Write the word to complete each sentence.

1. hiss hill

Jack and Jill go up a ____________.

2. pass pack

They ____________ a big log.

3. mock moss

It has ____________ on it.

4. eggs adds

The pals sit down to have some ____________.

5. mill mess

They make a ____________.

6. buzz buck

Some bugs come out and ____________ by.

7. ill off

Jack and Jill hop ____________ that log!

8. will wing

What ____________ they do?

9. huff hull putt puff

They ____________ and ____________ and run back down!

Name ______________________ Date ______________

Handwriting

High Frequency Words

Trace each High Frequency Word and then write it.

each each

no no

said said

saw saw

use use

was was

were were

who who

Spelling & Word Work

Word Cards: Words with *-ck, -ng*

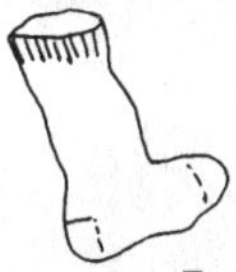 sock	 truck	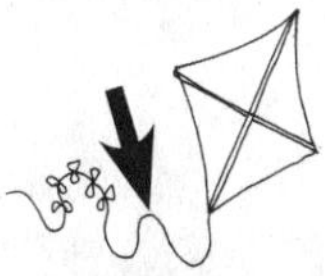 string	 building
black	duck	hung	trick
tackle	ring	fling	quick
hang	bang	slick	tickle
sing	thing	strong	rung
lock	flock	rock	song
lick	sung	long	nick

Spelling & Word Work

High Frequency Word Cards

like	when
but	said
so	no
this	use
if	was
that	were
he	saw
in	each
up	who

Name ______________________ Date ____________

Comparison Chart

Compare Media

Use this chart to compare "Be My Neighbor" and "My Favorite Place."

	Photo-Essay	Internet Bulletin Board
has photos	✓	✓
has captions		
has more than one writer		
gives facts		
asks and answers questions		
lets people share ideas and communicate		

Take turns with a partner. Ask each other questions about a photo-essay or an Internet bulletin board.

Name ________________________________ Date ______________

Phonics

Short Vowels

Circle the word that names the picture.

1.  cot cat cut	**2.** 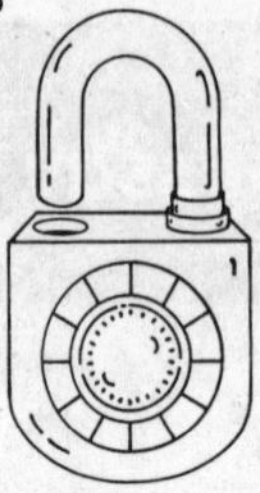 lock lick luck	**3.** 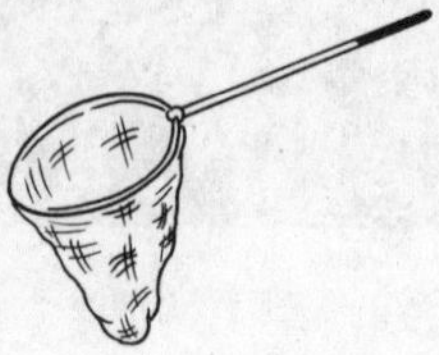 nut not net
4. 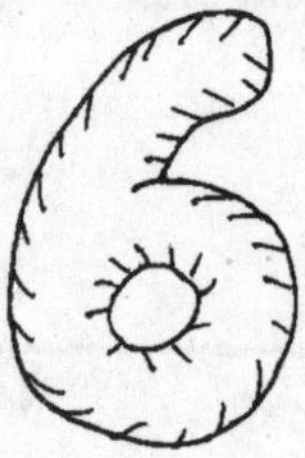 socks sax six	**5.** 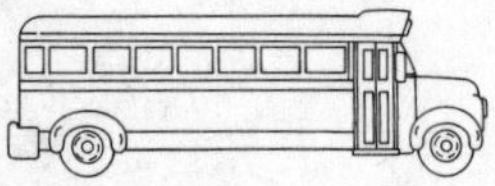 bus bass boss	**6.** 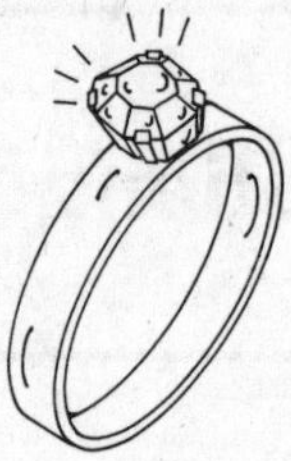 rung rang ring
7.  hit hat hut	**8.** 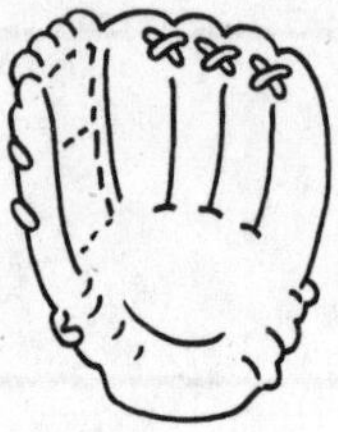 mat mitt mutt	**9.** 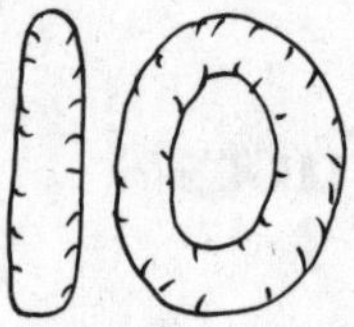 ten tan tin
10. 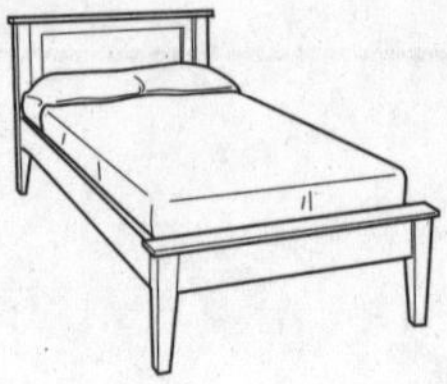 bud bad bed	**11.**  cup cap cop	**12.** 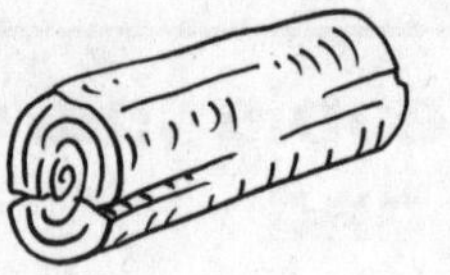 leg log lag

Read It Together I see six socks and a sax!

Name ______________________ Date __________

High Frequency Words

What Did We See?

Write a word from the box to complete each sentence.

High Frequency **Words**
each
no
said
saw
use
was
where
who

1. Matt said, "Can you tell what my pals ______________ pass by?".

2. Ming said, "They ______________ little."

3. Mack said, "Was ______________ one tan?"

4. Pam said, "______________. One was tan."

5. Lin said, "They ______________ their legs to hop."

6. Matt said, "What did my pals see? ______________ can tell us?"

Grammar: Possessive Nouns

Word Cards

	'	s	
house	street	neighborhood	friends
Mom	Dad	Grandmother	Grandfather
dogs	birds	trees	leaves
cars	trucks	sidewalk	park
ponds	bugs	zoo	animals
buildings	bus	trains	schools
playground	stores	bridge	Mr. Flores
Mrs. Brown	Dr. Adams	Capt. Smith	policewoman

Name ______________________ Date ______________

Phonics

Short Vowels

Write the words to complete each sentence.

1. big fills

Sid __________ his __________ basket with eggs.

2. pal runs

Then Sid __________ to find his __________ Ross.

3. ten has

Sid __________ __________ eggs for Ross.

4. did get

Where __________ Sid __________ the eggs for Ross?

5. pet got

He __________ them from his __________ hens!

6. sells but

Sid __________ some of his eggs, __________ not all of them.

7. packs not

He __________ up the eggs that he did __________ sell.

8. pan mix

His mom can __________ them up in a __________.

9. picnic will

Sid __________ have them at his __________. Yum!

Name ______________________ Date ______________

Grammar and Writing

Write Possessive Nouns and Abbreviations

Read the story. Then choose a word from the box that goes with each sentence.

Mr.	Jason's	Ling's
sister's	puppies'	neighbors'

I really like my neighborhood. Some of my neighbors' homes are big and some are small. My friend ________ house is across the street. It's big because he has eight brothers and sisters. My ________ boyfriend lives in a little house on the next block. He plays soccer with me sometimes. ________ Ling lives next door. I like to play with Mrs. ________ new puppies in their back yard. The ________ fur is very soft, but their tongues are rough!

Name ______________________ Date __________

Grammar: Proper and Possessive Nouns

Use Proper and Possessive Nouns

Grammar Rules Proper and Possessive Nouns

- A proper noun names a specific person, place, or thing. (Example: Texas)
- Some titles of people begin with a capital letter and end with a period. (Example: Dr.)
- A possessive noun names an owner. (Example: Jackson's)

Underline the proper nouns and write them in the chart. Then make each proper noun possessive. The first one is done for you.

Mrs. Preston lives in a neighborhood called Grandview. Her home is on Maple Street. Adam Preston is her son. We go to the same school. He is on my soccer team, too. Mr. Mohr is our coach.

Proper Nouns	Proper Possessive Nouns
Mrs. Preston	Mrs. Preston's

Write a sentence with a proper noun and a proper possessive noun. Read your sentence to a partner.

Name ______________________ Date ____________

Phonics

Blends with *r, l*

Circle the word that names the picture.

1.  tag flag drag	**2.** 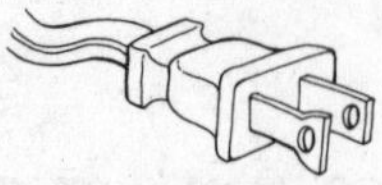 plug slug jug	**3.**  class glass grass
4. 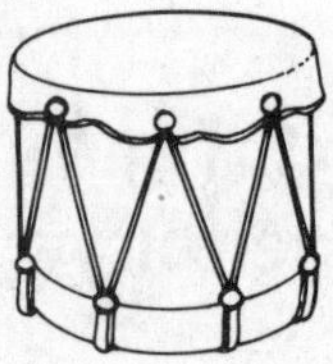 drum plum hum	**5.**  log clog frog	**6.**  truck cluck pluck
7.  flap trap clap	**8.**  bricks tricks flicks	**9.**  slab crab lab
10. 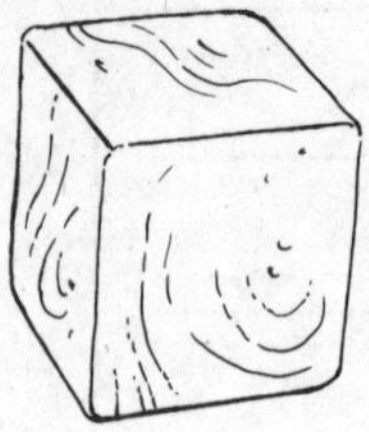 frock block clock	**11.**  grin win bring	**12.** 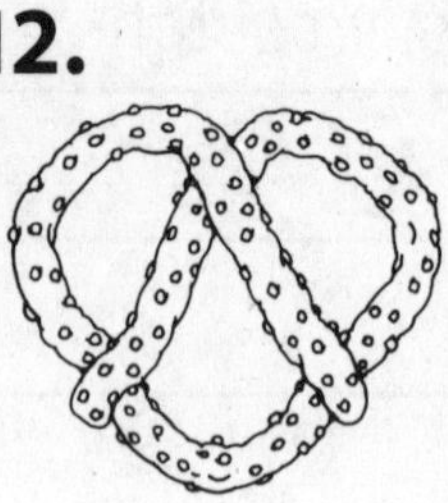 drill flannel pretzel

Read It Together Grin and clap if you like pretzels.

Name ______________________ Date ____________

Beginning-Middle-End Chart

The Nature Walk

Make a story map to tell about a nature walk.

Beginning:

How does the story start?

↓

Middle:

What happens next in the story?

↓

End:

How does the story end?

Share your Beginning-Middle-End Chart with your partner.

Name ______________________________ Date ______________

Phonics

Blends with *r, l*

Write the word that completes each sentence.

1. plus drums

Tran's dad has ________.

2. bless brass

Some of them are ________.

3. trumpet trot

Tran has a ________.

4. click plastic

It is not ________. It is brass!

5. bran plan

Dad and Tran have a ________.

6. truck pluck

Tran and Dad get into the red ________.

7. bring cling

They ________ their drums and trumpet.

8. glass class

Then they go to Tran's ________.

9. trap clap

All of Tran's pals ________.

Name ______________________ Date ____________

Handwriting

High Frequency Words

Trace each High Frequency Word and then write it.

these these

body body

back back

how how

eat eat

those those

way way

into into

Word Cards: Blends with *r, l*

 flag	 brick	 clock	 truck
flatten	plastic	trick	problem
black	grip	block	trap
dragon	frantic	click	slap
traffic	grass	slid	glad
crab	plan	printed	glob
blast	drop	slip	cracking

Spelling & Word Work

High Frequency Word Cards

what	way
help	back
people	eat
do	those
there	how
by	into
day	these
then	body

Name ____________________ Date ____________

Phonics

Blends with *s*

Circle the word that names the picture.

1.  stop flop snap	**2.** 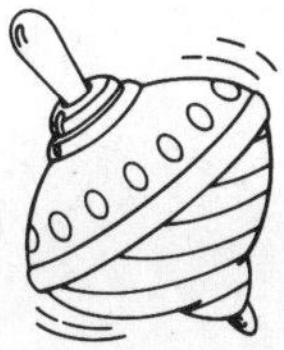 sting scan spin	**3.**  trim skim swim
4. 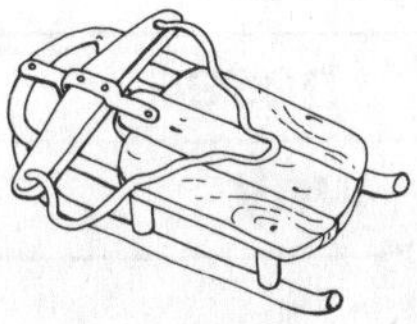 sped sled skid	**5.**  spell smell swell	**6.** 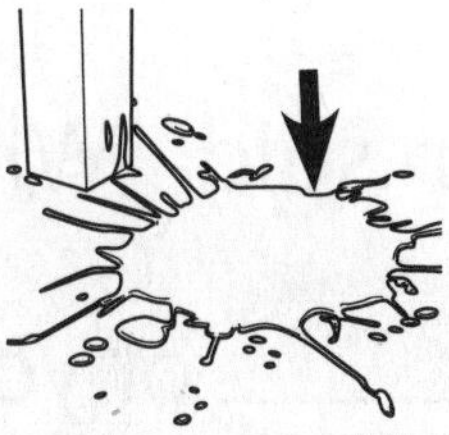 spill still frill
7. 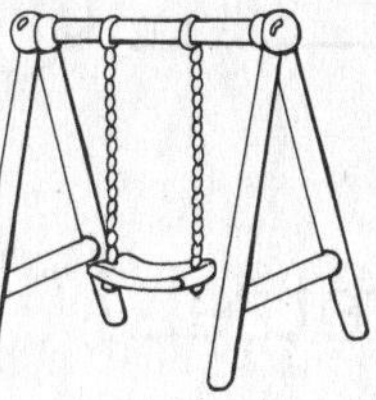 fling sling swing	**8.**  stack snack scuff	**9.** 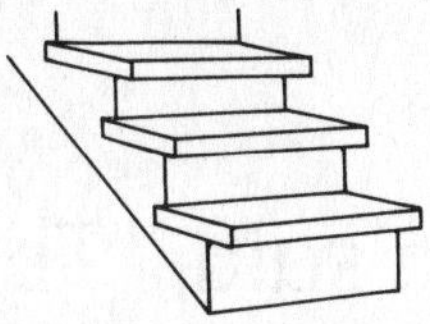 steps snaps snips
10.  skip slip clip	**11.**  stock slot spot	**12.**  slim stem skin

Read It Together Do you like to swim, skip, or swing?

Name ______________________________ Date ______________

High Frequency Words

A Pack of Pretzels

Write a word from the box to complete each sentence.

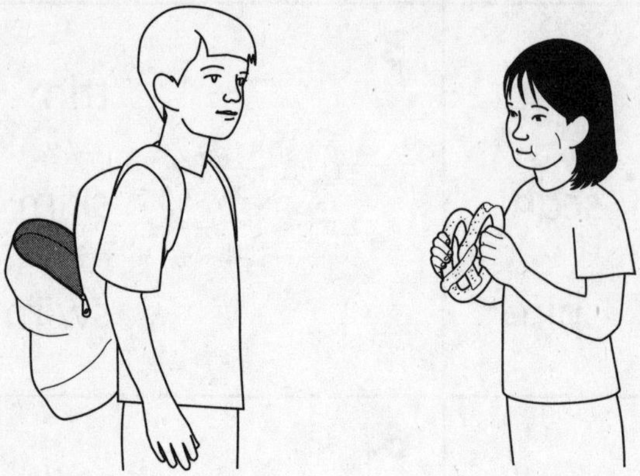

High Frequency Words
back
body
eat
how
into
these
those
way

1. Fran said, "What is in that pack on the ________ of your body?"

2. Fred said, "Look. I have a lot of stuff to ________ in it."

3. Fran said, "These are nuts. Are ________ pretzels?"

4. Fred said, "Yes. I like to snack on pretzels." ________ do you like them?

5. Fran bit ________ a pretzel.

6. Fran said, "I like them a lot! I will find a ________ to get pretzels, too!"

Name ______________________ Date ____________

Grammar: Main Verbs and Helping Verbs

Build Sentences

Cut out the cards and make a gray pile with the cards facedown. Spread out the white cards face up. Pick one gray card. Then choose a white card that matches the gray card you picked. Say a sentence using the word on the gray card and the word on the white card. Then put the cards on the bottom of the piles.

can	**might**	**do**	**does**
fly	**eat**	**think**	**run**
hold	**wish**	**drink**	**play**
hear	**see**	**taste**	**listen**
walk	**swim**	**imagine**	**touch**

Name ________________________ Date ____________

Phonics

Blends with *s*

Write the word that completes each sentence.

1. stiff sniff

The dogs ________ in the grass.

2. stick slick

One dog finds a ________ in the grass.

3. slot spot

One dog finds a ________ in the sun and naps.

4. smell swell

One dog sniffs. What can it ________?

5. slug snug

It smells a fox that is ________ in its den.

6. slop stop

Then the fox runs and will not ________.

7. still squid

The dog is ________, but looks at the fox.

8. spill speck

The fox runs until it is a little ________.

9. scans stacks

The dog ________ the grass. It cannot see the fox.

Name ______________________ Date ____________

Phonics

Triple Blends with *s*

Circle the word that names the picture.

1. 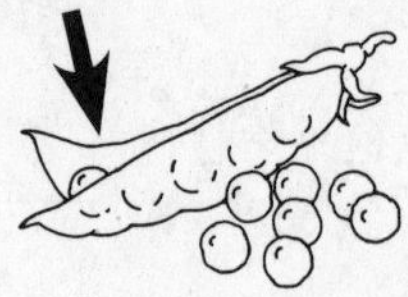 spot stick split	**2.** 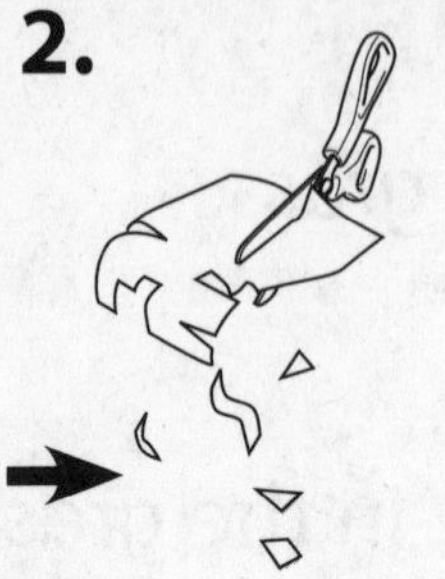 scraps stacks skips	**3.**  sting spring sling
4.  swing string sprig	**5.**  scrub stub scab	**6.** 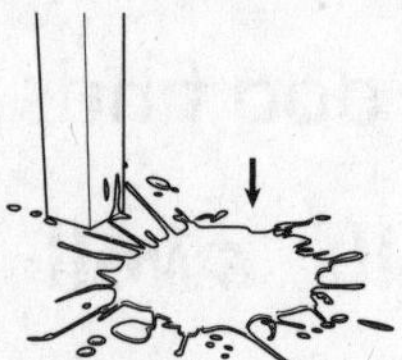 splat slat scat
7.  scram slum strum	**8.**  snap sap strap	**9.**  sprig swig strung
10. 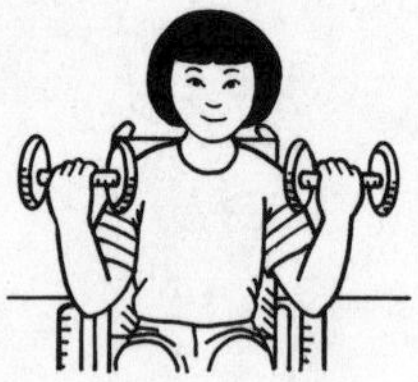 sprung strong scrod	**11.**  sprang stuck struck	**12.**  scruff stuff snuff

Read It Together The strong dog springs up, eats scraps, and scrams!

Name ______________________ Date ____________

Grammar and Writing

Write Action and Helping Verbs

Read the story. Then choose a word from the box that goes with each sentence.

carries	can fly	might sit
spot	sees	peep

An owl ___can fly___ without making any noise. This bird also __________ very well in the dark. A hunting owl __________ on a tree branch to look and listen for small animals. Hungry baby owls __________ impatiently for food. After catching its dinner, the owl __________ it back to its nest. If you __________ an owl, you have been very lucky!

Name ______________________ Date ____________

Beginning-Middle-End Chart

Twilight Hunt

Make a Beginning-Middle-End Chart to show the plot of "Twilight Hunt."

Beginning:

Screech Owl goes on a hunt. She must find food for her babies.

↓

Middle:

↓

End:

Use your Beginning-Middle-End Chart to tell your partner about "Twilight Hunt."

Name ______________________ Date ____________

Phonics

Final Blends

Circle the word that names the picture.

1.  plot plant plan	**2.** 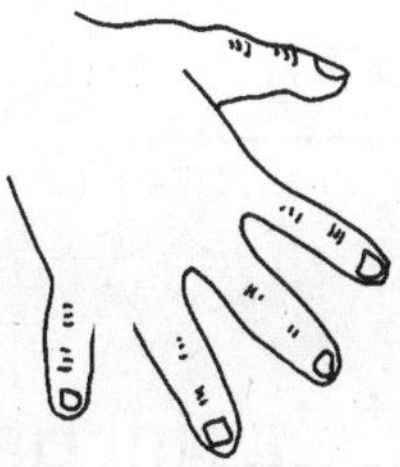 hand hack hang	**3.**  skin skit skunk
4. 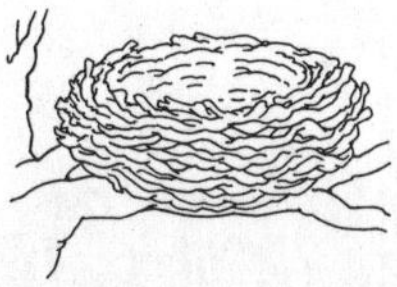 nest net neck	**5.** 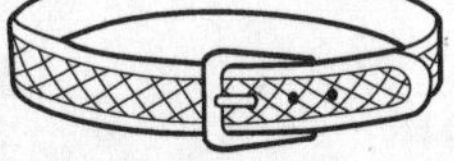 best bent belt	**6.** 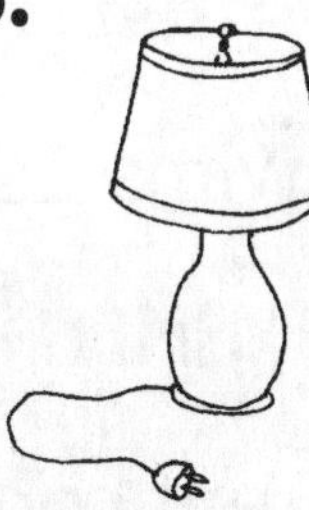 lamp land lack
7. 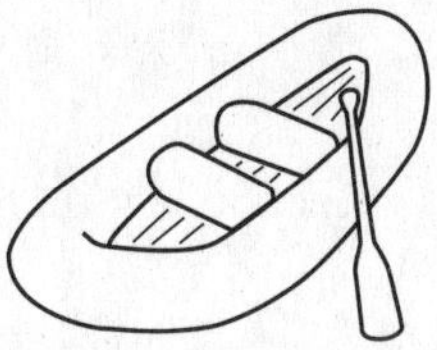 rang raft ramp	**8.**  deck dent desk	**9.** 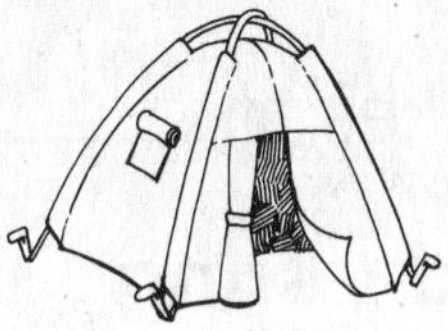 test tent tell
10.  bank bang band	**11.** 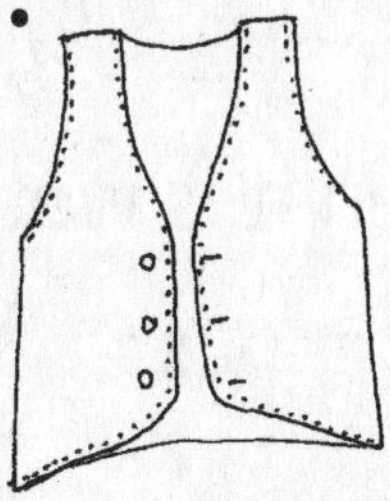 vent vend vest	**12.**  stamp stack stand

Read It Together Do you camp in a desk, a bank, or a tent?

Name ______________________ Date ______________

Phonics

Final Blends

Write the word that completes each sentence.

1. pot pond

Trent just got to the ________.

2. jump just

He will sprint down, ________ in, and get wet!

3. pant past

Trent swims ________ plants and frogs.

4. drink drift

Then Trent comes out and gets a ________.

5. gulp gust

He likes to ________ it down fast.

6. sand sang

Trent digs in the ________ for the rest of the day.

7. song soft

The sand is ________ when it is wet.

8. cast camp

Trent, his mom, and his dad ________ at the pond.

9. tent test

At the end of the day, they go into their ________.

Name ______________________ Date ______________

Handwriting

High Frequency Words

Trace each High Frequency Word and then write it.

could could

good good

hard hard

now now

over over

part part

under under

very very

Spelling & Word Work

Word Cards: Final Blends

 plant	 jump	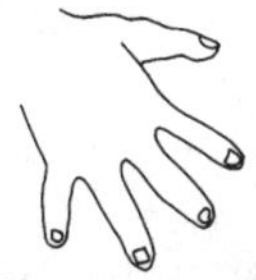 hand	 trunk
hunt	must	slant	fond
wind	insect	trust	connect
help	blend	blank	plump
bank	think	lost	stamp
drink	subtract	gulp	clamp
stand	pink	stunt	fact

Spelling & Word Work

High Frequency Word Cards

of	now
out	over
one	under
some	very
from	could
come	good
her	part
look	hard

Name ______________________ Date ____________

Venn Diagram

Compare Genres

Compare a story and a science article.

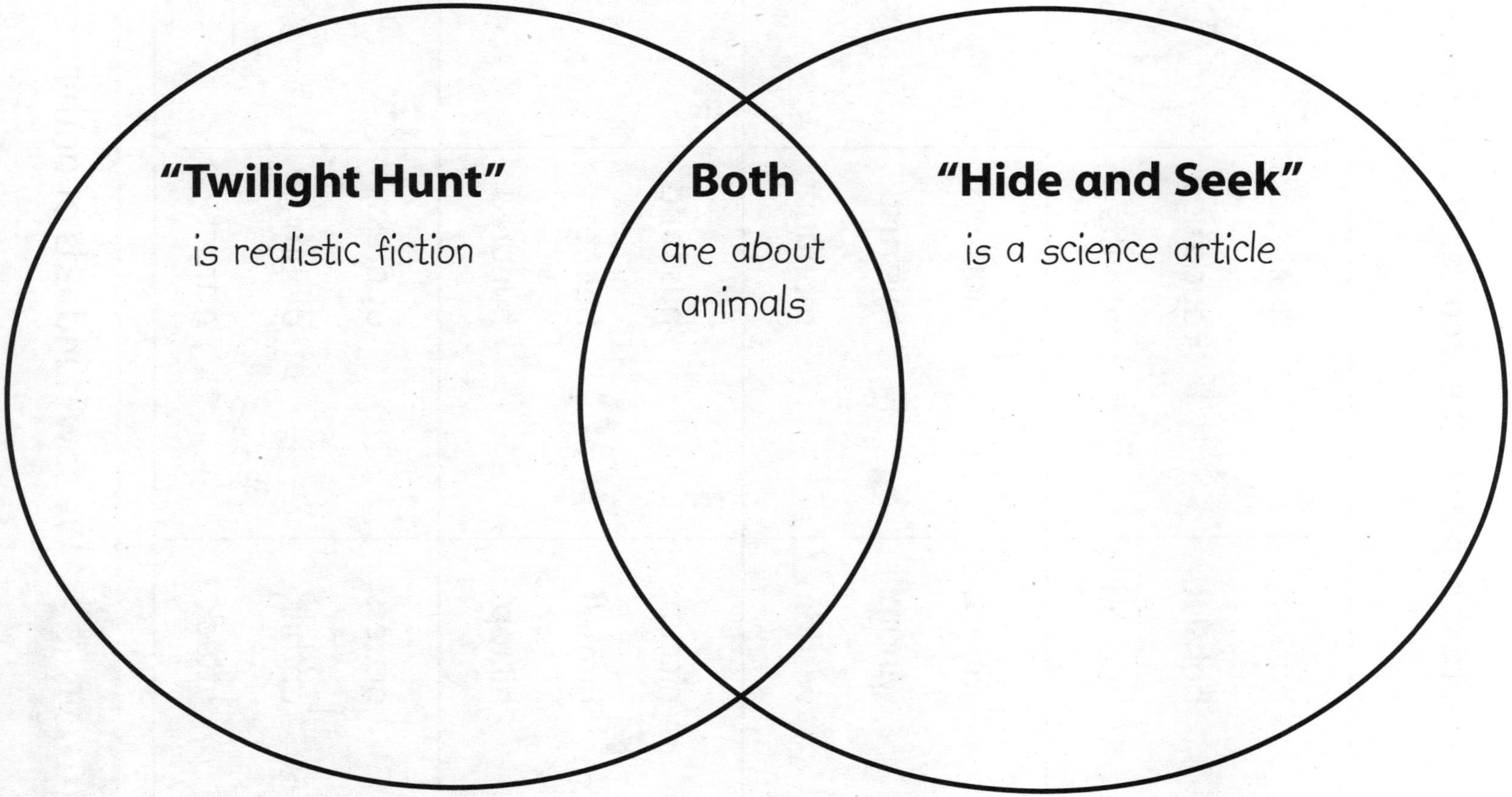

Share your diagram with a partner. Take turns telling about the story and science article.

Name ______________________ Date ____________

Phonics

Syllable Division

Circle the word that names the picture. Divide the word into syllables.

1.  basket bobsled backpack	**2.**  drumsticks ducklings dentists	**3.**  pumpkin public puppet
4.  witness windmill wisdom	**5.** 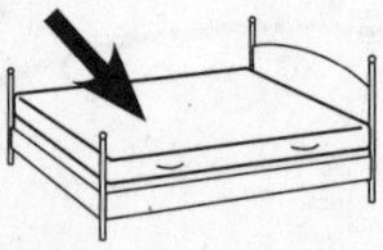 mattress mistrust manhunt	**6.**  handbag happen napkin
7.  hiccup himself hilltop	**8.** **100** husband helmet hundred	**9.** 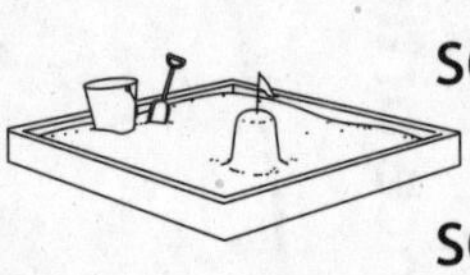 sandbox sapling sadness
10.  actress anthill attack	**11.**  address album attract	**12.** $10 - 7$ subset subject subtract

Read It Together We saw hundreds of anthills on the hilltop.

Name ______________________ Date ____________

High Frequency Words

Find the Backpack!

Write a word from the box to complete each sentence.

High Frequency **Words**
could
good
hard
now
over
part
under
very

1. Where ________ my backpack be?

2. It is ________ hard to find! Can you help me?

3. It is not ________ my bed or over my bed.

4. It is not on my desk! Where can I look ________?

5. Look at my jacket! I see a strap under it! Is the strap ________ of my backpack?

6. It is ________ that I have my backpack. Now where are my mittens?

Name ______________________________ Date ______________

Grammar: Helping Verbs

Use Helping Verbs

Directions:

1. **Make a spinner.**
2. **Play with a partner.**
3. **Take turns spinning the spinner.**
4. **Read the word you land on. Say a sentence using can, might, do, or does. Then have your partner say another sentence using the same helping verb and a different main verb.**

Make a Spinner

1. Put a paper clip in the center of the circle.
2. Hold one end of the paper clip with a pencil.
3. Spin the paper clip around the pencil.

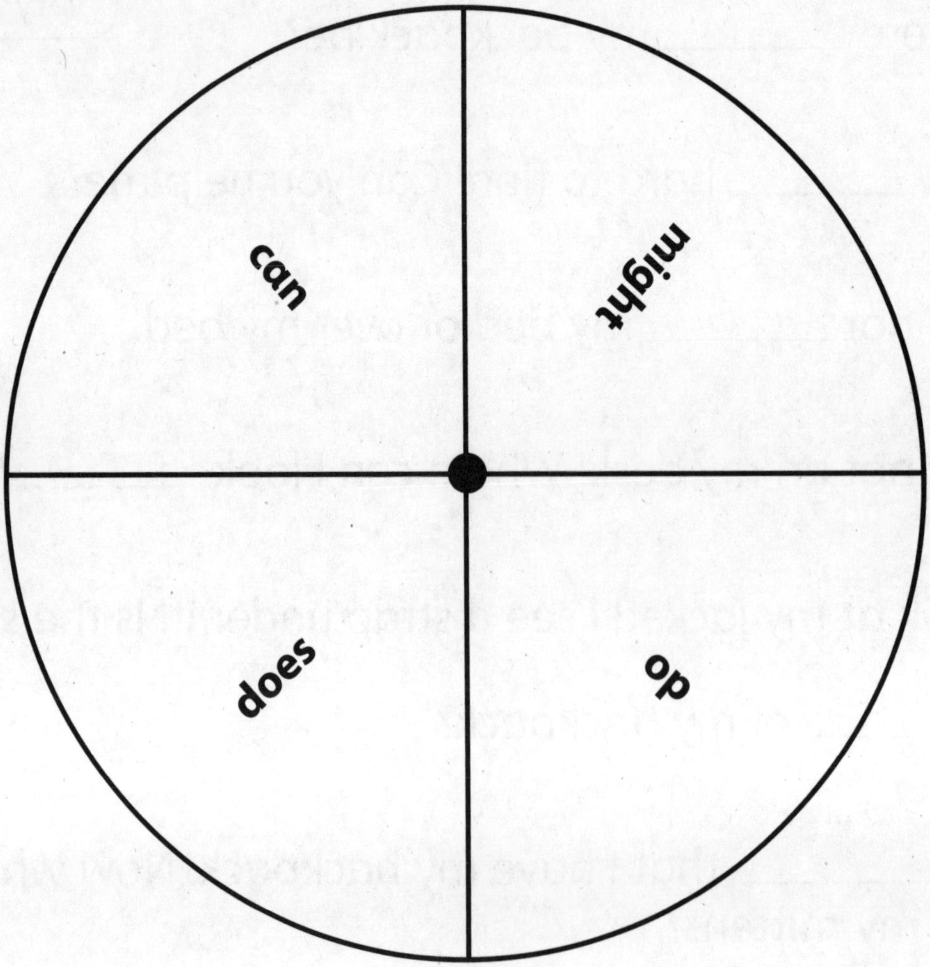

Name ____________________ Date ____________

Phonics

Syllable Division

Divide the words into syllables. Then write the word that completes each sentence.

1. **hilltop tantrum**

   Bess and Kent jog up to the __________.

2. **instant anthill**

   What do they see? Bess sees an __________!

3. **dentist inspects**

   Bess looks down and __________ it.

4. **address hundreds**

   She sees __________ of ants.

5. **ducklings subtracts**

   Kent sees six __________ in a pond.

6. **handful grandpa**

   Then Bess and Kent see their __________.

7. **backpack tundra**

   He gets a snack from his __________.

8. **pumpkin napkin**

   The snack is __________ muffins.

9. **helmets gumdrops**

   They eat muffins with __________ on top!

Name ______________________ Date ______________

Grammar and Writing

Write Helping and Action Verbs

Read the story. Choose a word from the box that goes with each sentence.

can	do	does
hide	look	might

Some animals can ___hide___ themselves to stay safe. An insect ____________ use color or shape to hide from its enemies. A mantis really ________ depend on its green color and leaf shape to hide. A little red fish does ________ exactly like the plants around it! Some birds ____________ blend in with the trees and flowers around them. If I look on leaves carefully, I __________ find a mantis or a katydid.

Name ______________________ Date __________

Grammar: Action and Helping Verbs

Roll a Verb

Grammar Rules Action and Helping Verbs

For Action Verbs

- Use **-s** at the end of an action verb if the subject is **he**, **she**, or **it**.
- Do not use **-s** for **I**, **you**, **we**, or **they**.

For Action Verbs with Helping Verbs

- A **helping verb** comes before the **main verb**.

Use a numbered game cube to play this game.

1. Roll the game cube. Find the helping verb that goes with the number.
2. Roll the game cube again. Find the action verb that goes with the number.
3. Say a sentence with the action verb and helping verb. The first player to use all six action verbs and helping verbs in sentences correctly wins.

Helping Verbs	Action Verbs
1. do	1. look
2. does	2. escape
3. can	3. fly
4. might	4. run
5. do	5. search
6. can	6. hide

Name ______________________ Date ____________

Phonics

Words with *ch, tch*

Circle the word that names the picture.

1.  chick brick quick	**2.**  camp catch cast	**3.**  past pack patch
4.  flunk chunk skunk	**5.**  branch hatch brand	**6.** 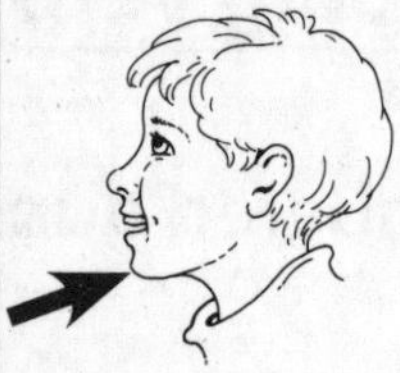 chin grin spin
7. 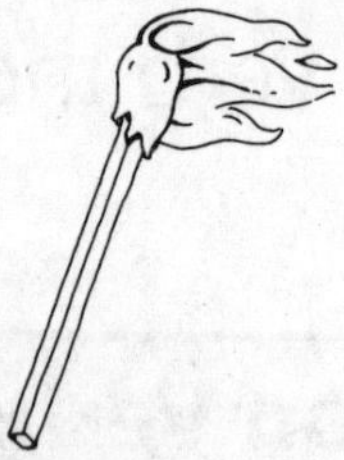 match mast mask	**8.**  drums strums chums	**9.**  crank crutch crust
10.  fleck speck check	**11.** 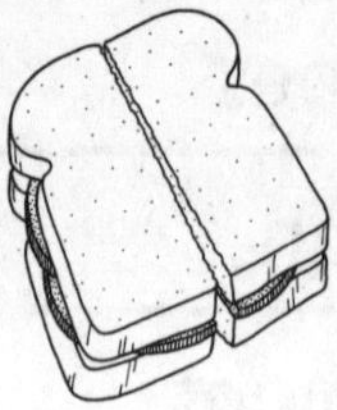 sandwich sapling such	**12.**  object ostrich chimp

Read It Together Chuck and his chums scratch their chins.

Name ____________________ Date __________

Comparison Chart

Creature Features

Compare animals and their features.

Features	Creature 1	Creature 2

Tell a partner how the animals are alike.

Name ______________________ Date ____________

Phonics

Words with *ch, tch*

Write the word that completes each sentence.

1. chipmunk trunk

A little __________ collects nuts.

2. chunk lunch

Will it eat the nuts for its __________?

3. children munch

I like to __________ on nuts, too!

4. chimp catch

A big __________ eats some nuts.

5. clump chomp

It likes to __________ on plants, bugs, and eggs, too.

6. chat sandwich

I eat an egg __________ for a snack!

7. ostrich odd

An __________ eats plants, sand, and bugs.

8. switch chicken

One of its eggs is like 24 __________ eggs. That is very big!

9. quench champ

It runs very fast, too. The ostrich is such a __________!

Name ______________________ Date ____________

Handwriting

High Frequency Words

Trace each High Frequency Word and then write it.

wait wait

know know

other other

warm warm

year year

yellow yellow

world world

without without

Word Cards: Words with *ch, tch*

 chest	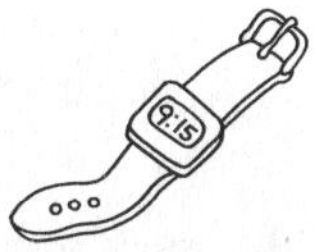 watch	 champ	 patch
itch	children	chimp	pitch
lunchbox	chatting	batch	check
chill	catch	fetch	stretch
chin	switch	attach	chick
scratch	kitchen	stitch	hatch
rich	bench	ditch	inch

Spelling & Word Work

High Frequency Word Cards

with	other
their	know
be	year
them	without
your	wait
down	warm
they	world
or	yellow

Name ______________________ Date ____________

Phonics

Words with *th, wh*

Circle the word that names the picture.

1. 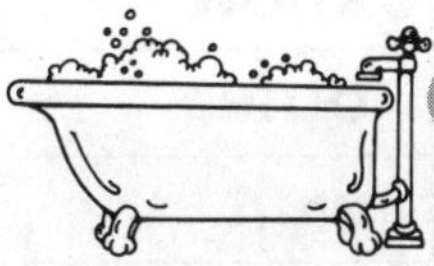 batch / bath / bank	**2.**  stink / think / drink	**3.** 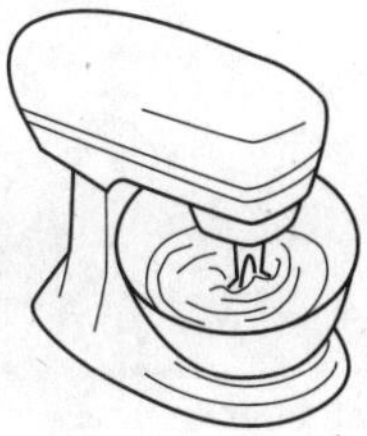 chip / trip / whip
4.  thick / trick / chick	**5.**  disk / frisk / whisk	**6.**  path / patch / past
7.  mops / moth / much	**8.**  track / black / whack	**9.**  math / match / mask
10.  thrill / still / frill	**11.**  stiff / whiff / cliff	**12.** 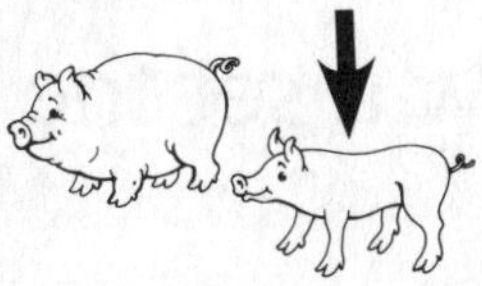 spin / chin / thin

Read It Together What do you think? Is a moth thick or thin?

Name ______________________ Date ____________

High Frequency Words

What Is It?

Write a word from the box to complete each sentence.

High Frequency **Words**
know
other
wait
warm
without
world
year
yellow

1. Each year, people all over the ________ see it. No one is without it.

2. I am ________ when I sit in it.

3. It looks ________ in the day and red when it sets.

4. I saw it set the ________ day.

5. If you ________ here, you can see it set, too.

6. Do you ________ what it is? It is the sun!

Name ______________________ Date ______________

Grammar: Use Has, Have, Had

Sentences: Has, Have, Had

Cut cards. Spread both the gray cards and the white cards face up. Choose one of each and say a sentence using those two words.

has	**have**	**had**

I	**you**	**he**	**she**
it	**we**	**they**	**cat**
dog	**horse**	**bird**	**fish**
wings	**tail**	**fur**	**feathers**
scales	**animals**	**pets**	**lions**
teeth	**friends**	**neighbors**	**parents**

Name ____________________ Date __________

Phonics

Words with *th, wh*

Write the word that completes each sentence.

1. sixth whiff

What is that smell? Did you get a ________ of it?

2. think wink

I ________ Dad is in the kitchen!

3. bring broth

That smell must be his chicken ________.

4. thing string

It is the best ________ to eat for lunch.

5. thick chick

It is not ________. It is thin.

6. then when

I eat it ________ it is still warm!

7. which stitch

There are buns and muffins, too. Dad asks ________ I want.

8. wink with

I will have a bun ________ my broth.

9. thank whisk

Then I ________ Dad for a very good lunch!

Name ______________________ Date ____________

Phonics

Contractions

she	+	is	=	she's
can	+	not	=	can't

Write the contraction for the two underlined words on the line.

1. You can see that he is sick.

You can see that ________ sick.

2. You can see that she is not sick.

You can see that ________ not sick.

3. Do you think it is fun to be sick?

Do you think ________ fun to be sick?

4. You can not be with your pals.

You ________ be with your pals.

5. You do not have much fun.

You ________ have much fun.

Name ____________________ Date __________

Phonics

Contractions

I	**+**	**am**	**=**	**I'm**
you	**+**	**are**	**=**	**you're**

Write the contraction for the two underlined words on the line.

1. I am in the pond.

   ________ in the pond.

2. You are in the pond, too.

   ________ in the pond, too.

3. We are all wet!

   ________ all wet!

4. My dog can not swim.

   My dog ________ swim.

5. We do not let my dog jump into the pond!

   We ________ let my dog jump into the pond!

Name ______________________ Date ____________

Grammar and Writing

Write Irregular Verbs

Read the letter. Then choose a word from the box that goes with each sentence.

were	have	had
has	was	is

Dear Brandon,

I am having a great time at sea camp. This camp has lots of cool things to do.

The water in the ocean ________ warm and clear. That means it is easy to see fish. Yesterday, I ________ fun on a boat. It ________ exciting to zoom through the waves. Seagulls and other birds ________ all around the boat. I will come home Saturday. I ________ a special surprise from sea camp for you!

Your friend,

Ali

Name ______________________ Date ____________

Comparison Chart

Living Lights

Make a chart to compare bioluminescent animals.

How It Uses Light	Animal
to attract prey	glowworm anglerfish
to send messages	
to hide	

Use your comparison chart to tell a partner about the animals in "Living Lights."

Name ______________________ Date ____________

Phonics

Words with *sh, ph*

Circle the word that names the picture.

1.  smell fell shell	**2.** 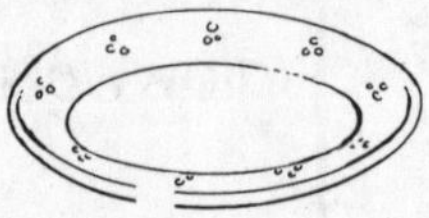 dish ding ditch	**3.**  shed bled sped
4. 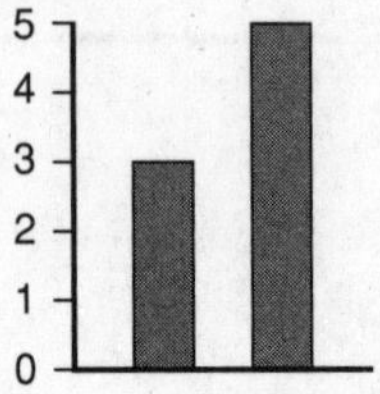 grass graph grand	**5.** 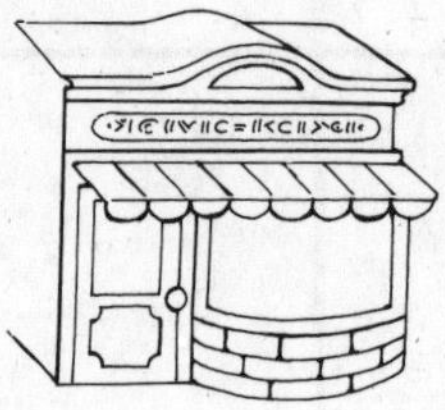 stop chop shop	**6.**  fish fill fist
7.  whip chip ship	**8.** 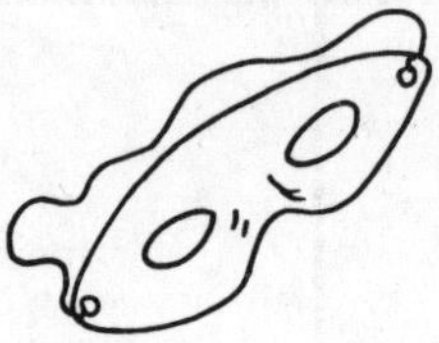 mask mash match	**9.** 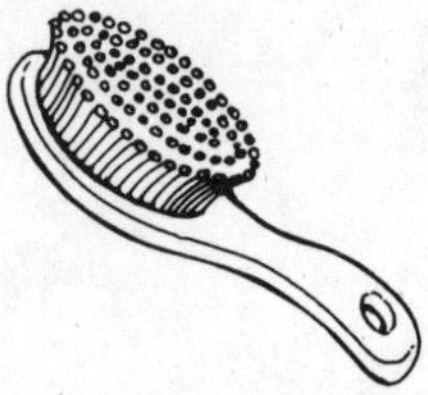 brunch brush brick
10.  split splash scratch	**11.**  shrub scrub stub	**12.**  tramp track trash

Read It Together She sells fish and shells at her shop.

Name ______________________ Date ______________

Phonics

Words with *sh, ph*

Write the word that completes each sentence.

1. **graph shellfish**

   We can see __________ in this tank.

2. **shells fresh**

   They have no fins. They have __________.

3. **shrimp squish**

   This tank has __________ in it.

4. **swish dolphins**

   Over here are the __________.

5. **shock fish**

   They swim, but they are not __________.

6. **mammals shrunk**

   They are __________ like you and me!

7. **shack splash**

   Look out! They will __________ and get you wet!

8. **dash damp**

   Now we __________ over to see the man in the tank.

9. **shelf wish**

   I __________ I could swim in the tank with him!

Name ________________________ Date ____________

Handwriting

High Frequency Words

Trace each High Frequency Word and then write it.

call call

more more

than than

two two

walk walk

why why

young young

because because

Spelling & Word Work

Word Cards: Words with *sh, ph*

 fish	 shell	 dolphin	 phlox
wish	graph	splash	phone
bush	phase	push	phrase
dash	phonics	wash	orphan
shift	elephant	she	trophy
shelf	shut	alphabet	shrug
Phil	ashen	photo	shop

Spelling & Word Work

High Frequency Word Cards

other	call
know	more
year	two
without	walk
wait	than
warm	young
world	why
yellow	because

Name ______________________ Date ____________

Comparison Chart

Compare Genres

Use a comparison chart to compare "Living Lights" and "Clever Creatures."

Features	"Living Lights"	"Clever Creatures"
is about animals	✓	✓
includes words that rhyme		✓
has facts		
has photographs		
has illustrations		

Work with a partner. Read each feature and see if it is in "Living Lights" and "Clever Creatures." Make a check if you see the feature.

Phonics

Words with *-ed, -ing*

Find the match for your card. Act it out.

jump	kick
blink	stretch
jumped	jumping
kicked	kicking
blinked	blinking
stretched	stretching

Name ______________________ Date ____________

High Frequency Words

Walking the Dog

Write a word from the box to complete each sentence.

High Frequency **Words**
because
call
more
than
two
walk
why
young

1. I have a ________ dog. My dog is still a pup.

2. I ________ with my pup each day.

3. On some days, we go on ________ than one walk.

4. We go on ________ walks.

5. I call my pup to me now. ________ do I call her?

6. I call her ________ we are going on a walk!

Name ______________________________ Date ______________

Grammar: Contractions

Use Contractions of *Be* and *Have*

Directions:

1. **Take turns with a partner.**

2. **Toss a marker onto the game board.**

3. **Follow the directions in the square your marker lands on.**

4. **After you say your sentence, your partner follows these steps:**

- **Say your partner's sentence with a contraction.**
- **Say your partner's sentence with a contraction and *not*.**
- **If your partner's sentence is singular, make it plural. If your partner's sentence is plural, make it singular.**

Say a sentence with am.	Say a sentence with is.
Say a sentence with are.	Say a sentence with has.
Say a sentence with have.	Say a sentence with had.

Name ______________________ Date ____________

Phonics

Words with *-ed, -ing*

Write the word with *-ed* or *-ing* to complete each sentence.

1. go

Gramps and Ben are __________ fishing.

2. want

Last year, Ben __________ to go, but he was too young.

3. pack

Ben just __________ all his fishing stuff.

4. help

Gramps __________ him.

5. stand

Now Gramps and Ben are __________ on the dock.

6. splash

The fish are __________.

7. pass

One big fish just __________ by them!

8. hand

Ben is __________ Gramps his fishing rod.

9. look

He is __________ at the fish. That is more fun than catching them!

Name ______________________ Date ______________

Phonics

Plurals *-s*, *-es*

Write the word with *-s* or *-es* to complete each sentence.

1. thing

What __________ will we see if we walk down this path?

2. fox

Look over there! I see two __________ in the grass.

3. branch

What is up in those __________?

4. nest

I see two __________.

5. egg

There are little __________ in them.

6. shrub

Do you see those __________ by the pond?

7. skunk

Some __________ are under them.

8. bench

We can sit on the __________ over there.

9. sandwich

Then we can eat __________ for lunch.

Name ______________________ Date ____________

Grammar and Writing

Write Full Forms of *Be* and *Have*

Read the report. Then choose words from the box that go with each sentence.

has not	they are	she had
I am	I have	is not

My name is Bella and ___I am___ interested in animals, especially insects. I think ________ very interesting. Did you know that not all bugs are insects? Insects have six legs. A spider ________ an insect because it has eight legs. I love to read books about insects. ________ just finished one about insects that change color. I loaned it to my sister Alex, but she ________ finished it yet. She said ________ already started another book, so my bug book would just have to wait!

Name ______________________________ Date ______________

Grammar: Verbs *be* and *have*

Insects at the Zoo

Grammar Rules Verbs *be* and *have*

Verbs should match who or what they are telling about.

For yourself, use	**am**	I **am** a scientist.
	have	I **have** work to do.
For one other person or thing, use	**is**	The Io moth **is** very clever.
	has	It **has** wings that look like big eyes.
For one other person, yourself and others, or other people and things, use	**are**	These wings **are** a clever trick.
	have	Many moths **have** features that keep them safe.

Choose the correct verb. Then read the sentence to a partner.

1. My teacher ___is___ interested in all kinds of insects.
   is / are
2. He ________ good news for our class.
   has / have
3. We ________ on our way to the zoo on Friday!
   is / are
4. The zoo ________ a special place to see insects.
   has / have
5. I ________ excited about the trip to the zoo.
   am / is
6. You ________ invited to come, too!
   is / are

Name ______________________ Date ____________

Phonics

Words with Long *a*

Circle the word that goes with each picture.

1. 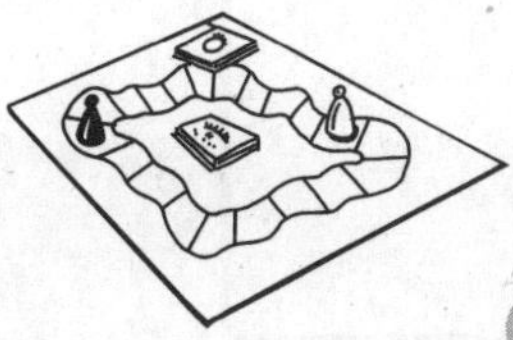 gap gum game	**2.** 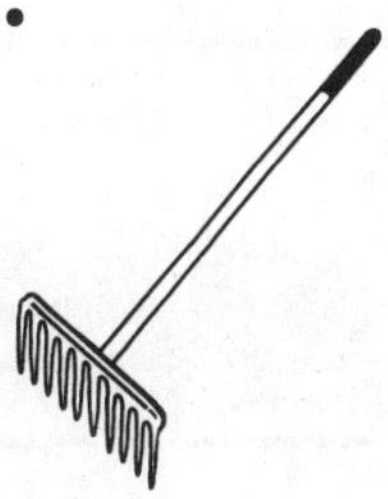 rake rack rock	**3.**  cane can cap
4. 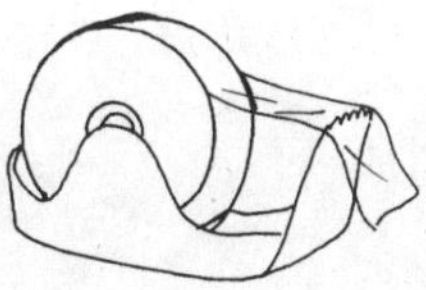 tape tip tap	**5.**  cap cape cup	**6.**  lack lake lock
7. 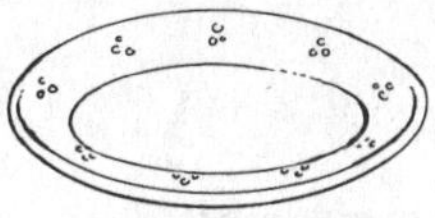 pluck plate pat	**8.** 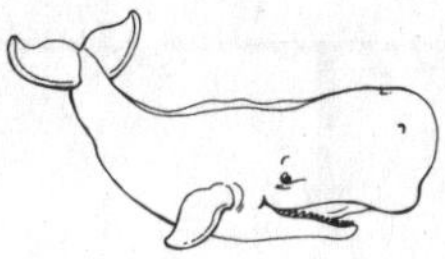 whale well whack	**9.**  snack snake snap
10.  brag brake brick	**11.** 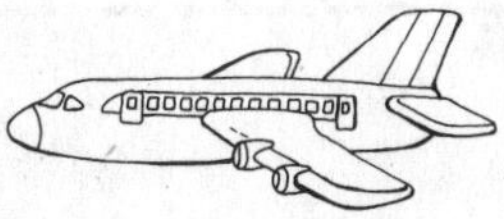 pan plan plane	**12.**  man mane mast

Read It Together Do you see waves or rakes in the lake?

Name ______________________ Date ____________

Problem-and-Solution Chart

Problem and Solution

Fill out a problem-and-solution chart.

Problem:

Event 1:

Event 2:

Solution:

Tell a partner about a problem you solved.

Name ______________________ Date __________

Grammar: Adjectives

Adjectives and Nouns

Find an adjective and a noun that rhyme from the word banks. Write the rhyming pair next to the riddle it answers.

Adjectives

dry	wet	gray
dark	swell	loud
nice	damp	

Nouns

cloud	ice	sky
camp	park	pet
day	well	

1. What is a soaked puppy called? a wet pet
2. What is smooth, frozen water called? ______________
3. What is a big tent after a rainfall called? a ______________
4. What is a rainy Monday called? a ______________
5. What is a playground during a strong storm called? a ______________
6. What is a lack of clouds called? a ______________
7. What is rumbling thunder called? a ______________
8. What is a great place to get water called? a ______________

Name ______________________ Date ____________

Phonics

Words with Long *a*

Write the word that completes each sentence.

1. wade cake

Zane and Jake ________ into the lake.

2. tack take

They ________ a quick dip and swim to the raft.

3. tapes waves

Then Mom ________ at them, and they swim back.

4. cave make

Zane finds a ________ in some rocks.

5. bats bakes

What is in it? Are there ________ and snakes?

6. manes chases

Jake ________ Zane back to Mom and Dad.

7. snack snake

They ________ on sandwiches.

8. states grapes

Then they eat a bunch of ________ .

9. trade late

It gets ________ . They pack up and go back to their van.

Name ______________________ Date ____________

Handwriting

High Frequency Words

Trace each High Frequency Word and then write it.

cold cold

form form

turn turn

drink drink

live live

water water

feel feel

three three

Spelling & Word Work

Word Cards: Long *a*

 lake	 game	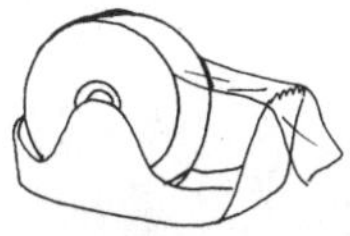 tape	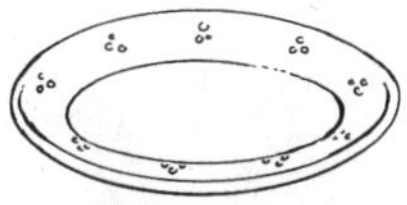 plate
date	shake	flake	came
shape	drape	state	snake
flame	wake	name	gate
late	same	take	frame
cape	crate	scrape	brake
skate	quake	blame	grape

Spelling & Word Work

High Frequency Word Cards

back	cold
how	drink
those	feel
body	form
into	live
way	three
eat	turn
these	water

Name ______________________________ Date ______________

Phonics

Syllables

Circle the word that goes with each picture.

1.  channel chase champs	**2.**  panes pancakes pandas	**3.**  scallop scab skate
4.  cascade cape cupcake	**5.**  frame frank frantic	**6.** 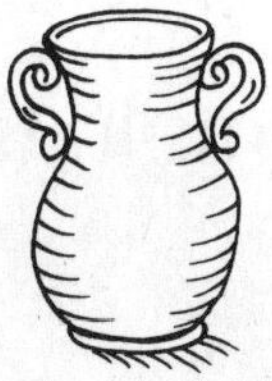 vase invade vane
7.  upstate unmade upset	**8.**  exam exit exhale	**9.**  snack snake snap
10. 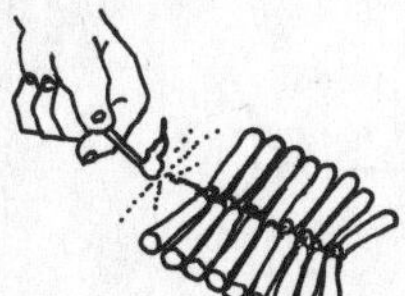 unsafe unlace subtract	**11.**  end escape engrave	**12.** 2 + 2 = 3 make mistrust mistake

Read It Together Do you like cupcakes or pancakes?

Name ______________________________ Date ______________

High Frequency Words

At the Lake

Write a word from the box to complete each sentence.

High Frequency Words
cold
drink
feel
form
live
three
turn
water

1. Jane swims in the ______________ at the lake.

2. It feels very ______________ .

3. Fish live in the lake. Jane sees ______________ swim by.

4. Then they ______________ back and swim by Jane.

5. Jane gets out of the lake and has a ______________ of water.

6. This ______________ of water is good to drink!

Name ______________________ Date ______________

Phonics

Syllables

Divide each word into syllables. Then write the word that completes each sentence.

1. **invade nickname**

   I am Jackson, but my ____________ is Jack.

2. **shameful escape**

   Mom smiles and says the things I do are ____________ .

3. **unmade exhale**

   She does not like it when my bed is ____________ !

4. **translate mistake**

   I made a big ____________ when I let the dog escape!

5. **inhales pancakes**

   Then there was the big mess when I made ____________ !

6. **unsafe inflate**

   I spilled milk, and she said the mess was ____________ .

7. **cupcakes inflates**

   But Mom has a big hug and ____________ for me. Yum!

Name ______________________ Date ____________

Grammar and Writing

Write Adjectives

Adjectives That Describe		Adjectives That Compare		Adjectives That Signal	
fresh	a lot	faster	fastest	this	that
huge	bright	bigger	biggest	these	those
yellow	three	softer	softest		

Read the adjectives on the chart. Choose adjectives to complete the sentences.

1. Rain did not fall for ___three___ weeks.
2. The sun was ______________ and hot.
3. We want to catch rain in pails by ______________ porch.
4. The round pail is ______________ than the square pail.
5. A ______________ cloud forms in the dark sky.
6. Rain! ______________ water from that cloud fills our pails.

Name ______________________________ Date ____________

Vocabulary

Vocabulary Bingo

1. Write one Key Word in each cloud.
2. Listen to the clues. Find the Key Word and use a marker to cover it.
3. Say "Bingo" when you have four markers in a row.

Name ________________________ Date ____________

Problem-and-Solution Chart

Frog Brings Rain

Use a problem-and-solution chart to tell about "Frog Brings Rain."

Problem: First Woman needs Water to put out Fire.

↓

Event 1: She asks Hunting People to take Water to Fire.

↓

Event 2:

↓

Solution:

Use your chart to tell a partner how First Woman and Frog solve the problem.

Name ______________________________ Date ______________

Phonics

Words with Long *i*

Circle the word that names the picture.

1. 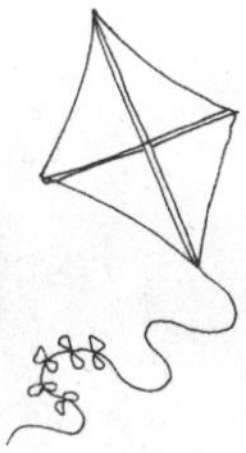 kite kit Kate	**2.**  dim desk dive	**3.**  rid ride rod
4.  like lick lake	**5.**  bat but bite	**6.**  nine nap name
7. 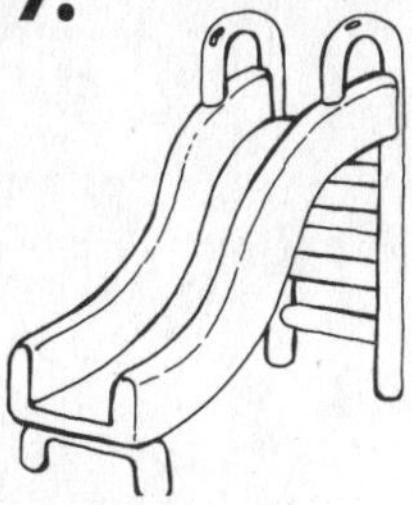 slide sled sling	**8.** 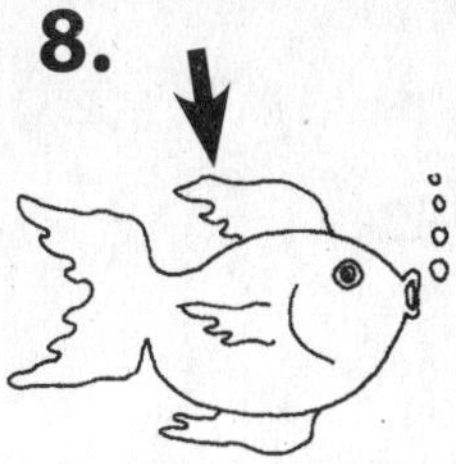 fine fin fan	**9.**  smell smile smash
10. 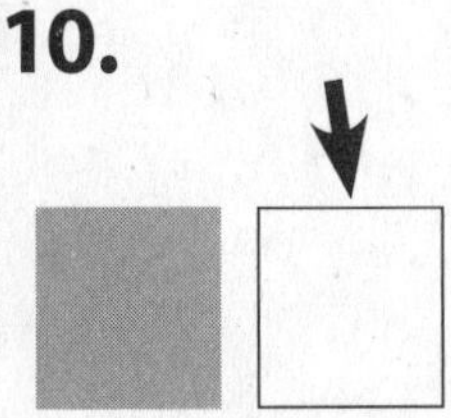 wit went white	**11.** 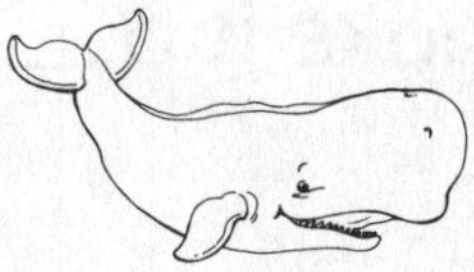 whale while will	**12.**  have hive hide

Read It Together Do you like to use a kite, a bike, or a slide?

Name ______________________________ Date ____________

Phonics

Words with Long *i*

Write the word that completes each sentence.

1. life beside

Mike and his dad sit ________ their tent.

2. dine wide

They ________ on fish, rice, and grapes.

3. size while

Mike sees a snake ________ they eat.

4. bite sunshine

The snake does not ________ Mike.

5. hides miles

It ________ in some rocks.

6. lines describes

Mike ________ the snake to his dad.

7. rise reptile

Dad tells Mike that a snake is a ________.

8. bedtime prize

Now it is late. It is ________.

9. five inside

Mike and Dad rest ________ their tent.

Name ______________________ Date ____________

Handwriting

High Frequency Words

Trace each High Frequency Word and then write it.

after after

away away

before before

carry carry

does does

give give

put put

through through

Spelling & Word Work

Word Cards: Long *i*, Short *i*

 pine	 prize	 hit	 rip
strike	insist	outside	glide
combine	sit	hide	pride
hid	dip	quip	side
wipe	like	whine	shine
pick	strict	trick	lip
mitten	napkin	drip	brick

Spelling & Word Work

High Frequency Word Cards

now	put
over	give
under	does
very	away
could	before
good	after
part	through
hard	carry

Name ______________________ Date __________

Comparison Chart

Compare Explanations

Show how the two explanations for rain are different.

How Is Rain Made?	
Traditional Tale Explanation	**Science Experiment Explanation**
• Frog carries water.	• Warm, wet air rises.

Ask a partner questions about the story and the science experiment.

Name ______________________ Date ____________

Phonics

Words with Long *o*

Circle the word that names the picture.

1. 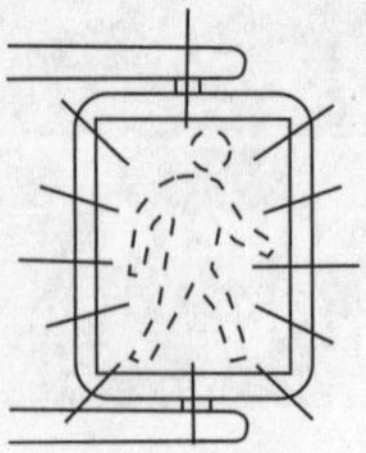 got go get	**2.** 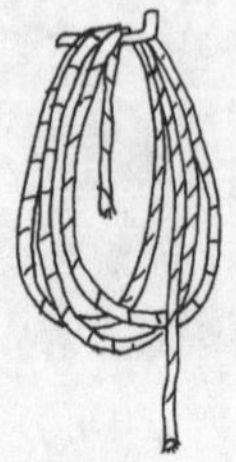 rob ripe rope	**3.**  dime dome dame
4.  globe glob glide	**5.**  haze has hose	**6.**  cone cane con
7.  hip hope hop	**8.**  stock stove stack	**9.**  phone fine phlox
10.  raze rose rise	**11.**  male mile mole	**12.**  not note no

Read It Together Do you water with a hose, a rose, or a stove?

Name ______________________________ Date ______________

High Frequency Words

In the Bag

Write a word from the box to complete each sentence.

High Frequency Words
after
away
before
carry
does
give
put
through

1. Mom and Dad ________ a bag.

2. They ________ it down and step away from it. What's inside the bag?

3. "________ us some hints," we beg.

4. So, ________ we look, Dad does.

5. "It does not have legs, and it swims ________ water," Dad says.

6. ________ we get those hints, we know it is a fish!

Name ______________________ Date ____________

Grammar: Adjectives and Articles

Mix and Match Sentences

Choose one item from each column. Say a sentence using all three parts. Then ask your partner to say the same sentence, changing one part.

A	B	C
a an the	hour river rain cloud well hole honest	ruined my plans is very deep that Dad dug is moving swiftly covers the sun passed by slowly person I know your new shoes runs by the town will stop soon has a cover on it is a long time hides the moon is big and dark holds lots of fish is good for our garden has a bucket on a rope wait by the park

Name ______________________________ Date ______________

Phonics

Words with Long *o*

Write the word that completes each sentence.

1. throne go

I ________ on a hike at camp.

2. tadpoles closes

We see some ________ in the pond.

3. so froze

They look ________ much like little fish.

4. quote suppose

I ________ they will be frogs one day!

5. holes explodes

Look over there! Do you see the ________ by those stones?

6. moles trombones

Do you think they were made by ________ or snakes?

7. opposes pinecones

We see twigs and ________ that came down in the wind.

8. broke flagpole

Now it is time to go and sit beside the ________.

9. rotate home

Then it will be time to get on the bus to go ________.

Name ______________________________ Date ______________

Grammar and Writing

Write Adjectives and Articles

Read the story. Then write a word from the box to complete each sentence.

dry	hungry	wet	a	an	the	those

Brodie and his family decided to go for ___a___ hike. The hike would take several hours. Brodie took ________ apple and a granola bar in his backpack. Hiking always made him ________.

After hiking for a while, Brodie's mom looked up at ________ sky. "Uh-oh," she said. "Look at ________ dark clouds. We might get ________." "No way!" answered Brodie. "My poncho will keep me ________."

Name ________________________________ Date ______________

Grammar and Writing

After the Storm

Grammar Rules Adjectives and Articles

An **adjective** can describe what a noun is like. →	A **light** rain starts to fall. The raindrops feel **icy** and **cold**.
An **article** can tell which noun you mean. →	**A** cloud fills up with water. Raindrops fall on **the** green hill. It is **an** amazing thing to see.

Add adjectives and articles.

The storm lasted for ___three___ days. Then the __________ sun rose. It dried up the __________ grass. __________ puddles started to disappear. Then we looked up into the __________ sky. There was __________ amazing rainbow. It looked __________ and __________. Soon the weather was __________ and __________ again.

Tell a partner about weather you like. Use adjectives and articles.

Name ______________________ Date ____________

Phonics

Words with Long e

Write the letters to name each picture.

1.

we

2.

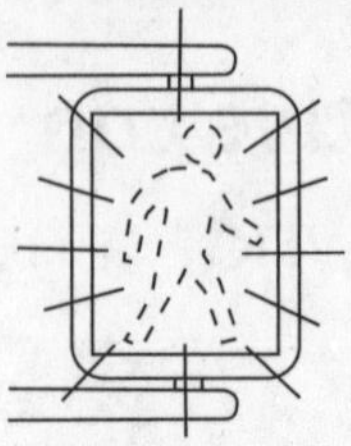

g

3.

h

4.

sh

5.

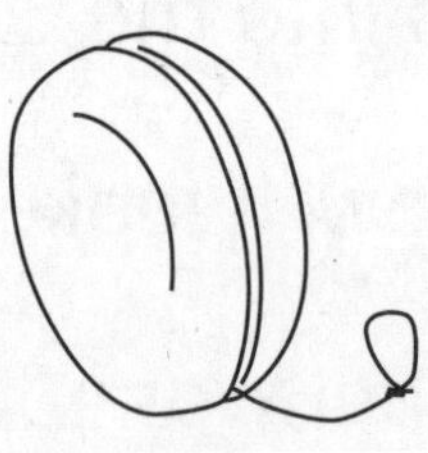

y -y

6.

P t

Read It Together We go to get Pete's yo-yo.

Name ______________________________ Date ______________

Cause-and-Effect Chart

Cause and Effect

Fill out a cause-and-effect chart to show what happened when you did something.

Cause		Effect
	→	

Tell a partner about what happened and why.

Name ______________________ Date ____________

Phonics

Words with Long e

Write the word that completes each sentence.

1. theme Eve

One of my classmates is ________.

2. We Extreme

________ like to run each day.

3. she these

Did you know that ________ runs very fast?

4. egg athlete

My pal Steve is an ________, too.

5. Concrete He

________ pitches to help win games.

6. Pete be

His pitches can ________ very fast.

7. me stampede

One day Steve pitched to ________.

8. complete see

I struck out, but Steve pitched a ________ game!

Name ______________________________ Date ______________

Phonics

Syllables

Write short vowel words from the box under *pen* and long vowel words under *so*.

he	not	no	be	cap	sun
web	him	hi	leg	she	go

pen **so**

1. ______________ **7.** ______________

2. ______________ **8.** ______________

3. ______________ **9.** ______________

4. ______________ **10.** ______________

5. ______________ **11.** ______________

6. ______________ **12.** ______________

Name ______________________ Date ____________

Handwriting

High Frequency Words

Trace each High Frequency Word and then write it.

our our

stop stop

take take

off off

clean clean

let let

think think

going going

Word Cards: Long *e*, Short *e*

 me	 we	 bed	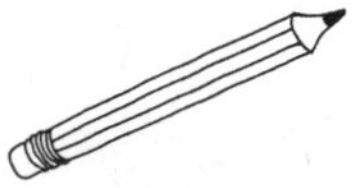 pencil
these	tennis	she	met
bell	Pete	get	here
complete	well	stampede	relax
web	felt	before	wet
decide	he	swell	begin
cobweb	theme	fell	men

Spelling & Word Work

High Frequency Word Cards

other	off
know	going
year	clean
without	stop
wait	think
warm	our
world	let
yellow	take

Phonics

Endings *-s, -ed, -ing*

Cut out the cards and mix them up. Match the cards and tell how the ending changes the word.

wave	**waves**
waved	**waving**
hop	**hops**
hopped	**hopping**
smile	**smiles**
smiled	**smiling**

Name ______________________ Date ____________

High Frequency Words

Mop It Up!

Write a word from the box to complete each sentence.

High Frequency **Words**
clean
going
let
off
our
stop
take
think

1. It is time to ________ our home.

2. I am ________ to help mop.

3. I ________ that is a fun job to do.

4. Mom and Dad ________ me fill the bucket with water.

5. Suds pop up. I turn the water off, but I can't ________ the suds! They go all over!

6. I have to ________ my mop and wipe up the suds!

Name ______________________________ Date ____________

Grammar: Adverbs

Say Sentences

Directions:

1. Make a spinner.
2. Play with a partner.
3. Take turns spinning the spinner.
4. Say a sentence using the adverb on the spinner.
5. Then your partner says a sentence using the same adverb.

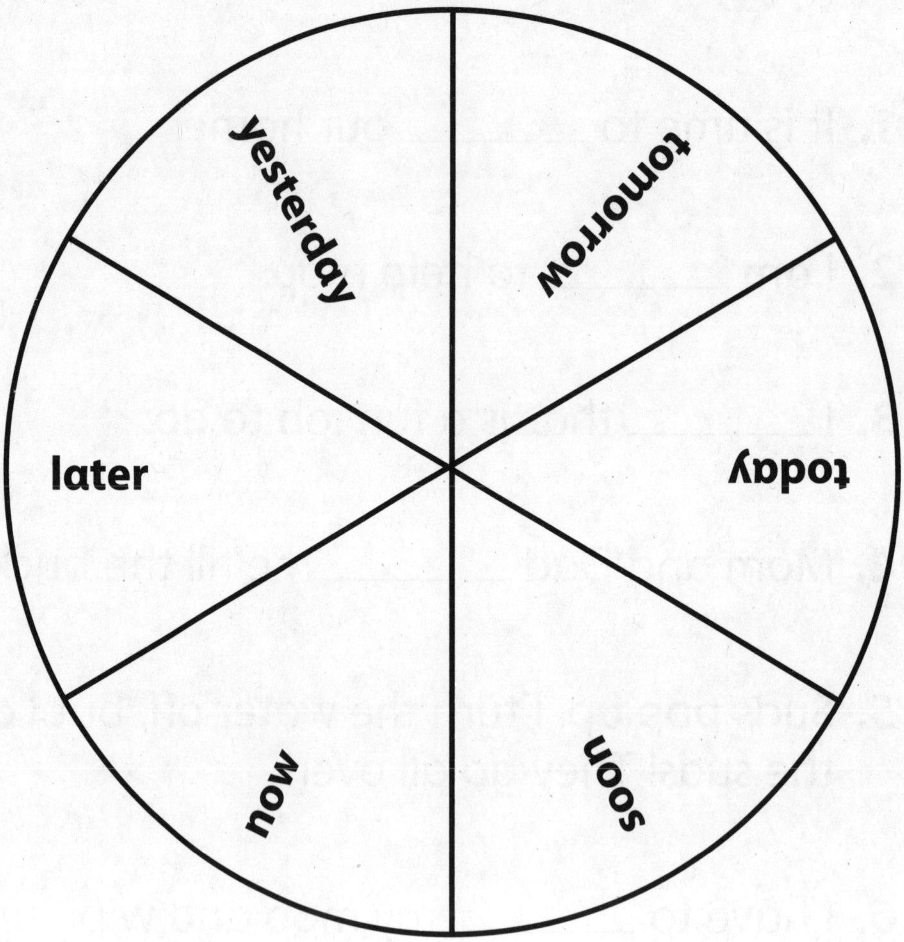

Make a Spinner

1. Put a paper clip in the center of the circle.
2. Hold one end of the paper clip with a pencil.
3. Spin the paper clip around the pencil.

Name ______________________ Date __________

Phonics

Endings *-s, -ed, -ing*

grin + s = grins	bake + s = bakes
grin + n + ed = grinned	grin + n + ing = grinning
bake - e + ed = baked	bake – e + ing = baking

Write the word with the correct ending to complete each sentence.

1. run

Tam is ________ on the path.

2. wave

She just passed her pal Ben and ________ to him.

3. stop

Ben was skating but had ________ to rest.

4. smile

When Tam ran by, Ben ________ at her.

5. chase

Now Ben hops up and is ________ Tam. Will he catch her?

6. get

The two pals are ________ close to the end of the path.

7. hope

Tam runs fast and ________ that she will win!

Name ______________________ Date __________

Grammar and Writing

Write Adverbs

Read the letter. Then choose a word from the box that goes with each sentence.

soon	swiftly	yesterday	quickly	slowly

Dear Megan,

Our rafting trip was awesome! I had so much fun yesterday. The river ran ________, but we still tried to paddle. We sometimes got splashed, but we dried out ________ in the sun. Now I have to walk ________ because all my muscles hurt. I hope I can go rafting again really ________, though.

Your friend,

Kate

Name ______________________________ Date ______________

Cause-and-Effect Chart

Cause and Effect

Fill out a cause-and-effect chart to show the results of things that happened in "PlayPumps."

Cause		Effect
Kids ride on the PlayPump and turn the wheel.	→	

Use your chart to tell a partner about more causes and effects in "PlayPumps."

Name ______________________ Date ____________

Phonics

Words with *u_e*

Circle the word that names the picture.

1.  mile mole mule	**2.** 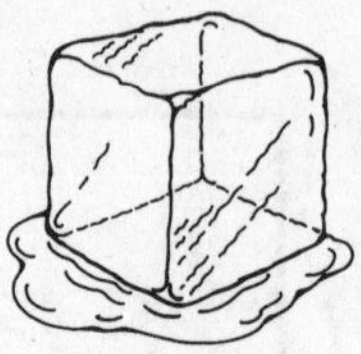 cube cub cab	**3.**  cap cup cape
4. 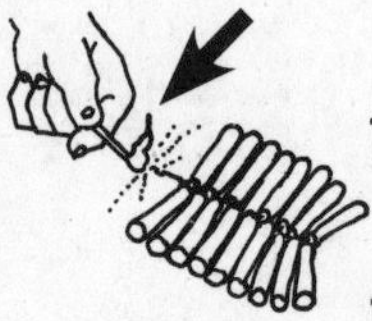 fuse fuss fist	**5.**  fine fun fan	**6.**  cap cute cut
7.  use us as	**8.** 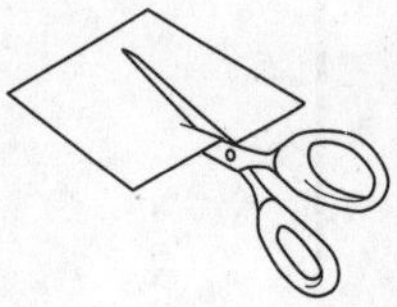 cut cute cat	**9.** 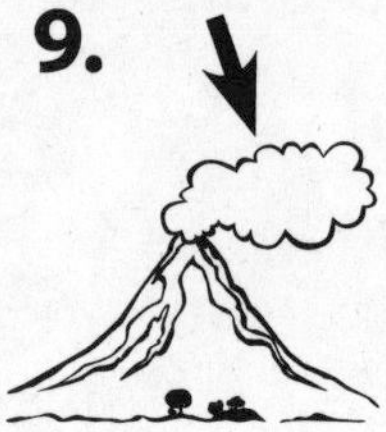 fun fame fume
10.  commute combat comma	**11.**  muffin mute munched	**12.**  command compact computer

Read It Together Do you think that a mule is cute?

Name ______________________ Date ____________

Phonics

Words with *u_e*

Write the word that completes each sentence.

1. commutes cubes

Dave __________ to his job each day.

2. dispute mule

He doesn't ride a __________ to his job in the city.

3. fuse bus

He rides a __________.

4. fumes ducklings

On some days, there are a lot of __________ from the bus.

5. Excuse Truck

One day a man stopped Dave and said, "__________ me."

6. confused tugged

The man was __________ because he was lost.

7. hundred used

Dave __________ a map to help the man find his way.

8. shrug cute

Dave has a __________ little dog.

9. pup accuse

When Dave is at his job, I take his __________ for walks.

Name ______________________ Date ____________

Handwriting

High Frequency Words

Trace each High Frequency Word and then write it.

city city

hold hold

land land

mile mile

much much

river river

sea sea

wash wash

Word Cards: *u_e*

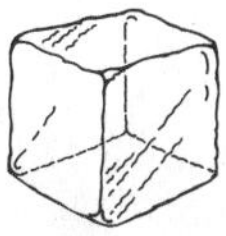 cube	 mule	 flute	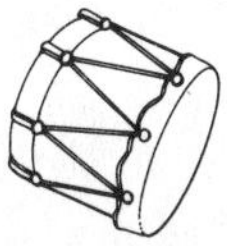 drum
hut	sun	use	fuse
cute	fume	mutt	tub
put	club	compute	excuse
stuck	include	tube	rude
June	glum	cut	prune
hug	spruce	bun	fun

Spelling & Word Work

High Frequency Word Cards

call	land
more	wash
two	city
walk	much
than	river
young	hold
why	sea
because	mile

Name ________________________________ Date ______________

Comparison Chart

Compare Information

Use a comparison chart to compare "PlayPumps" and "The Mighty Colorado."

How People Get Water	
"PlayPumps"	**"The Mighty Colorado"**
• Kids play.	

Share your chart with a partner. Take turns asking questions about the information.

Name ______________________________ Date ____________

Phonics

More Words with *u_e*

Circle the word that names the picture.

1. 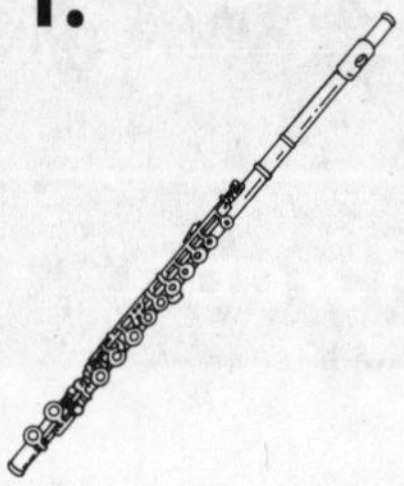 flake flute flunk	**2.**  rod rude ride	**3.**  tube tub tab
4. 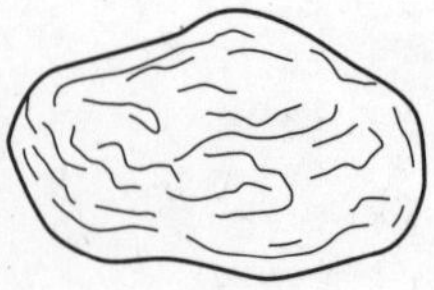 prune prone print	**5.**  tent tune tine	**6.**  crust crude crab
7. 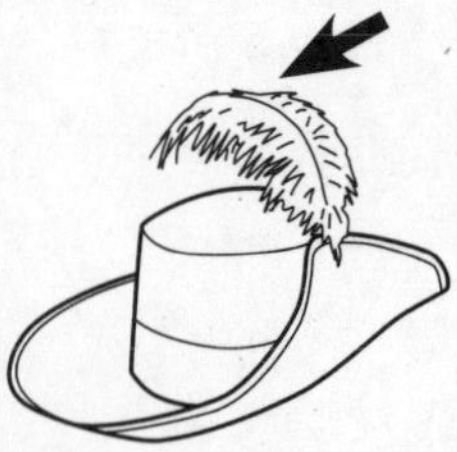 plant plum plume	**8.**  June jam just	**9.**  dens dines dunes
10.  like Luke lake	**11.** 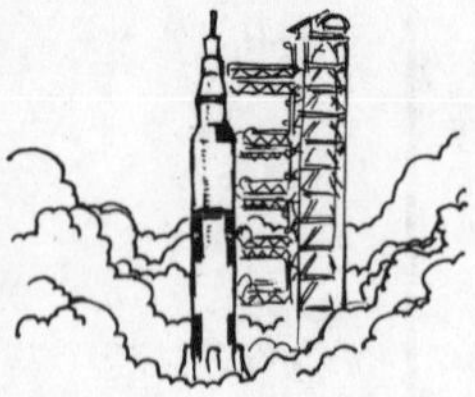 rocket rule role	**12.**  confuse complete costume

Read It Together One rule is not to be rude.

Name ______________________________ Date ______________

High Frequency Words

Home by the Sea

Write words from the box to complete each sentence.

High Frequency **Words**
city
hold
land
mile
much
river
sea
wash

Can you come to my home in the ________ next June? There is so ________ to see where I live. If we walk one ________ to the west, we can walk in the sand by the sea. Then we can ________ off the sand in the water. We can ________ hands, jump into the cold water, and swim in the waves. If we walk the other way, we can see ________ and water in a ________. I hope you can come to see me!

Name ______________________________ Date ______________

Grammar: Adjectives and Articles

Mix and Match Sentences

First choose a word from column A. Then choose one of the words in column B. Then choose words from column C and say a sentence using all three parts and any other words you want to add. You can change the form of the words in column C if you need to.

A	B	C
I	loud	walk
you	badly	yell
he	quick	write
she	carefully	stop
it	good	play
we	quietly	run
they	well	shout
person	quiet	read
	bad	sing
	quickly	go
	careful	eat
	loudly	fix

Name ______________________________ Date ______________

Phonics

More Words with *u_e*

Write the word that completes each sentence.

1. flutes dunes

My class is going on a trip to the sand ________.

2. includes prunes

The trip ________ time for hiking and time for lunch.

3. intrudes rules

Mr. Chang gave us some ________ for the trip.

4. tunes costumes

We may sing ________ on the bus, but we may not yell.

5. rude excuse

We must not be ________ to each other and to people we see.

6. pollute plume

We must not ________ while we are there, and we must take our trash back to the bus with us.

7. assumes tubes

He ________ that we will be good!

8. mules concludes

He ________ that if we are good, we will all have fun.

Name ______________________________ Date ______________

Grammar and Writing

Write Adverbs

Read the letter. Then choose a word from the box that goes with each sentence.

here	there	somewhere	well	smoothly	swiftly

Max was riding on a little raft through the Grand Canyon. The river rushed swiftly through the canyon. The family rafting trip was going __________. After some rough water, the raft was gliding __________ down the river. Max heard a loud sound __________ high over his head. He looked in the sky and saw a big hawk flying up __________. *I cannot believe I am* __________, thought Max. *I am as happy as that hawk must be.*

Name ______________________ Date ____________

Grammar: Adverbs

Adverb Tic-Tac-Toe

1. **Play with a partner.**
2. **Player 1 chooses and reads the sentence. Player 2 tells if the adverb tells how or when.**
3. **Player 2 marks the square if the answer is correct.**
4. **Then players switch roles.**
5. **Keep taking turns to see if one player can get three marks in a row.**

The water stopped yesterday.	We quickly called the plumber.	The plumber arrived soon.
The plumber worked carefully to find the clog.	She finally found the clog.	Then she cleared it up.
Slowly the water began to flow.	We have plenty of water today.	We gladly fill our water jugs.

Name ______________________________ Date ______________

Phonics

Words with *ai, ay*

Circle the word that names the picture.

1. 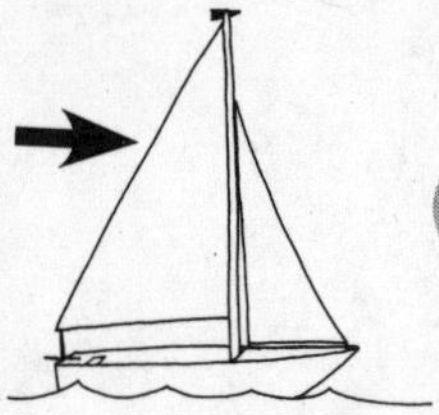 sell sail sill	**2.** 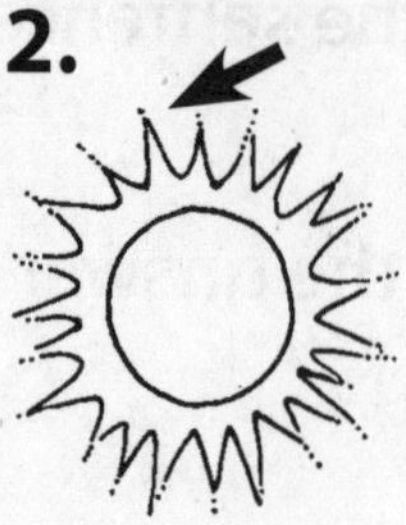 ray rat rail	**3.**  may mill mail
4.  ran rain rake	**5.**  hit hail hay	**6.**  jail jay jell
7. 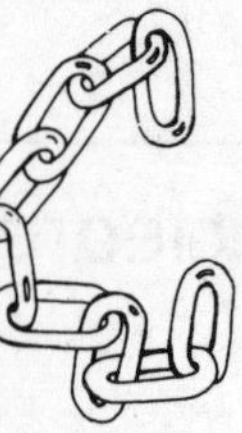 chain chin children	**8.** 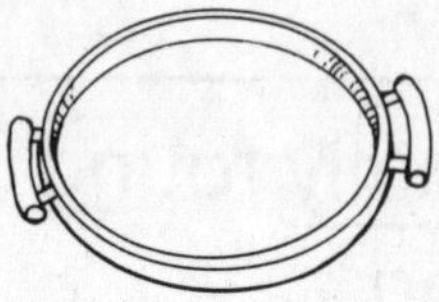 trap trail tray	**9.** 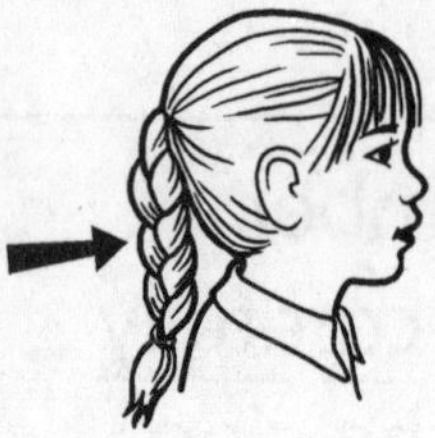 bray braid brad
10. 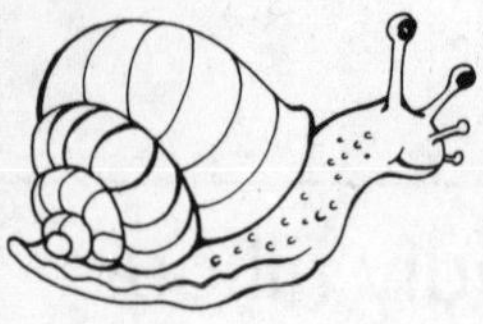 snack say snail	**11.**  paint pant pays	**12.** 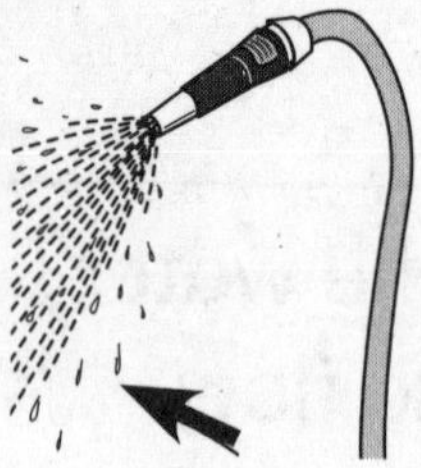 sprain spray sprint

Read It Together Jay paints trains on gray days when it rains.

Name ____________________ Date __________

Character Map

Character Traits

Make a character map. Write about two characters you know.

Character	What the Character Does	What the Character Is Like

Tell a partner which character was your favorite and why.

Name ____________________ Date __________

Phonics

Words with *ai, ay*

Unscramble the word and use it in a sentence.

1. a h y ___ ___ ___ ________________ ________________	**2. n i r a** ___ ___ ___ ___ ________________ ________________
3. i a l s ___ ___ ___ ___ ________________ ________________	**4. y a w** ___ ___ ___ ________________ ________________
5. y c a l ___ ___ ___ ___ ________________ ________________	**6. t i n a r** ___ ___ ___ ___ ___ ________________ ________________
7. t i w a ___ ___ ___ ___ ________________ ________________	**8. s l y p a** ___ ___ ___ ___ ___ ________________ ________________

Name ______________________ Date ____________

Phonics

Syllables with *ai, ay*

Divide the syllables. Circle the word that names the picture.

1. 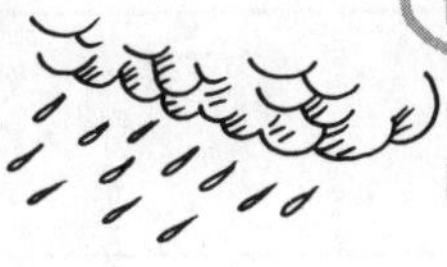 raining / resting	**2.**  fainted / painted	**3.**  playing / paying
4.  mailing / rushing	**5.**  braided / waited	**6.** 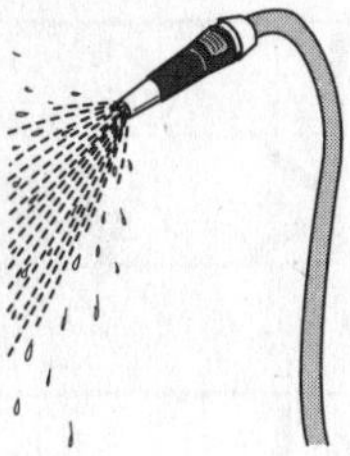 spraying / staying
7.  saying / sailing	**8.**  paying / playing	**9.**  staying / saying

Read It Together We like playing when it is raining.

Name ______________________________ Date ______________

Handwriting

High Frequency Words

Trace each High Frequency Word and then write it.

don't don't

door door

about about

work work

should should

want want

where where

important important

Spelling & Word Work

Word Cards: Words with *ai, ay*

 rain	 train	 hay	 spray
aid	sprain	main	yesterday
stain	tray	day	hail
maintain	pail	play	fail
waiting	paid	pain	say
stay	regain	away	plain
delay	decay	pray	always

Spelling & Word Work

High Frequency Word Cards

live	don't
feel	door
water	about
cold	work
drink	should
turn	want
three	where
form	important

Name ______________________________ Date ______________

Phonics

Syllable Division

Divide the syllables. Circle the word that names the picture.

1.

ostrich
oven
open

2.

zigzag
zebra
zapped

3.

email
even
enter

4.

melon
misses
moment

5.

racket
rapid
radish

6.
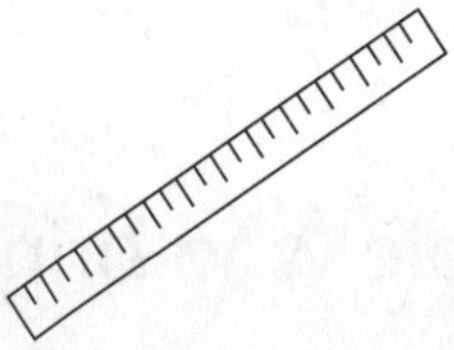
robot
rotate
ruler

7.

satin
salad
setup

8.

minus
music
menu

9.

cabin
comet
cobra

10.

second
seven
solid

11.

robin
relax
remake

12.

debate
dolphin
donut

Read It Together Is there a zebra or a radish in the salad?

Name ________________________________ Date ______________

High Frequency Words

Who Brings the Mail?

Write a word from the box to complete each sentence.

High Frequency Words
about
don't
door
important
should
want
where
work

1. People who bring mail have an __________ job to do.

2. They __________ hard, and we should thank them!

3. They __________ bring mail on Sundays.

4. My mailman puts mail in the box by my __________.

5. __________ does your mail go?

6. I want to find out more __________ this job because I want to be a mailman!

Name ______________________ Date ______________

Grammar: Sentences

Mix and Match Sentences

First choose a naming part from column A. Then choose a telling part from column B. Say a complete sentence using both parts and any other words you want to add.

A	B
girl	tumble
people	save
eggs	snatch
lion	fly
mouse	yell
he	catch
they	go
farmer	help
animals	live
eagle	smash
wall	cry
rocks	chew

Name ______________________________ Date ______________

Phonics

Syllable Division

Divide the syllables. Write the word that completes each sentence.

1. frozen photo

Can you find me in this _________?

2. female panic

I am the _________ who is playing the trombone!

3. minus music

I play all kinds of _________ on my trombone.

4. even exit

I can _________ play some jazz.

5. email seven

In fact, I will play _________ jazz songs for you!

6. oval second

The _________ song is the one I like best.

7. moment bison

Wait for one _________.

8. begin panic

Now I will _________ to play.

9. comics never

I hope that I _________ stop playing my trombone!

Name ______________________ Date ____________

Grammar and Writing

Write Complete Sentences

Read the story. Then choose the word or words from the word box that correctly complete each sentence. Write the words.

the little things	somebody
am going to the animal shelter	my sister and I
could not take care of themselves	we

Today I am going to the animal shelter. ____________ both help clean the shelter and play with the dogs and cats. ____________ dropped off a box of kittens last night. The tiny kittens ____________. ____________ mewed loudly and tried to climb out of their box. ____________ picked them up and fed them from a bottle.

Name ______________________ Date ____________

Character Map

Aesop's Fables

Make a character map to tell about the characters in "Aesop's Fables."

Character	What the Character Does	What the Character Is Like
the lion	lets the mouse leave	generous
Farmer Bean		

Use your character map to tell a partner about the characters in "Aesop's Fables."

Name ______________________________ Date ______________

Phonics

Words with *ee*

Circle the word that names the picture.

1. 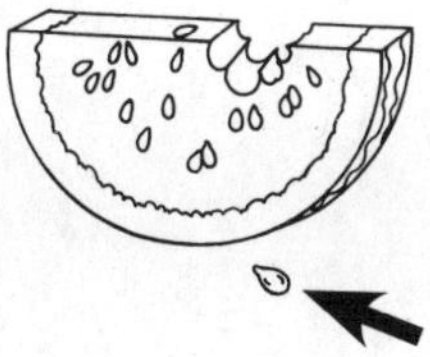 seed say sell	**2.**  quick quail queen	**3.**  best bay bee
4. 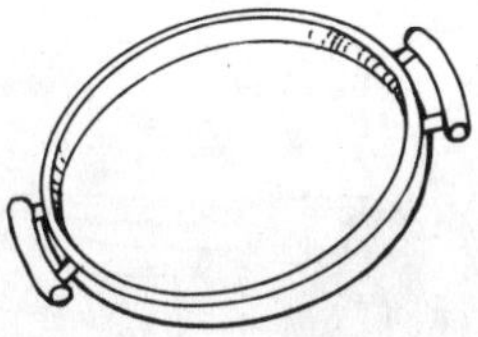 tree tray train	**5.** 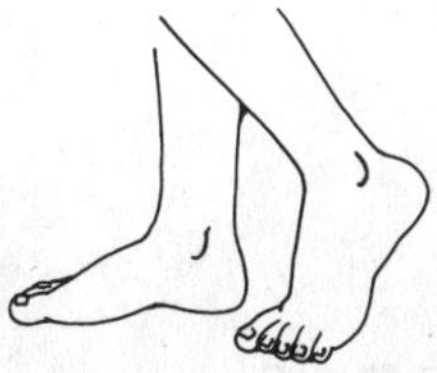 feet fell faint	**6.**  beet bait bet
7.  sled sleet sleep	**8.** 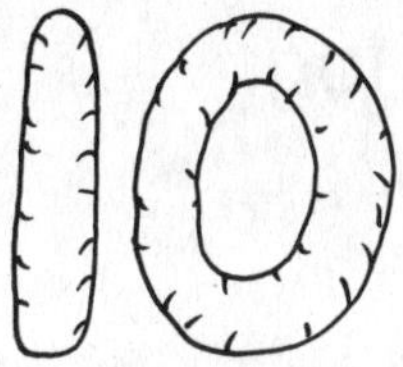 ten teen tone	**9.** 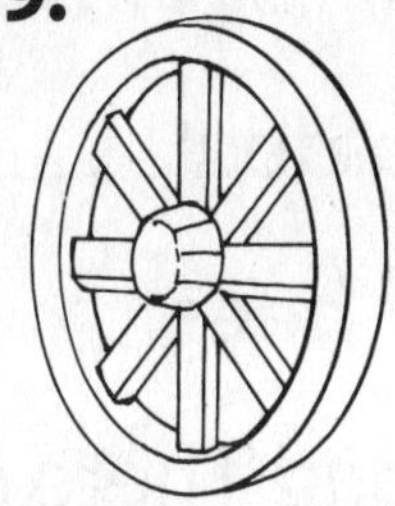 whale wheel while
10.  shop shape sheep	**11.**  tail teeth tenth	**12.**  strut stripe street

Read It Together Sixteen sheep sleep by the street.

Name ____________________ Date ____________

Phonics

Words with ee

Write the word that completes each sentence.

1. grin green

Dad and I sit under a big ________ tree.

2. trip tree

We see a robin in the ________.

3. cheeps chaps

It ________ its song.

4. twists tweets

A second robin ________ back.

5. peeks seems

My big dog ________ at a log.

6. bets bees

Look out! There are ________ in the log!

7. leek lake

My dog runs to the ________ and jumps into the water.

8. creeps crayons

Then he ________ up to me.

9. slaps sleeps

He shakes himself off, plops down, and ________.

Name ______________________ Date __________

Phonics

Contractions

I	+ would	= I'd
she	+ will	= she'll
they	+ have	= they've

Write the contraction that completes each sentence.

1. I would like a lemon muffin.

_______ like a lemon muffin.

2. Look! They have got three muffins on a plate.

Look! _______ got three muffins on a plate.

3. I think she will take one plain muffin.

I think _______ take one plain muffin.

4. I see that you have got one nut muffin.

I see that _______ got one nut muffin.

5. I know there will be one lemon muffin left for me!

I know _______ be one lemon muffin left for me!

Name ______________________ Date ______________

Handwriting

High Frequency Words

Trace each High Frequency Word and then write it.

house house

kind kind

place place

both both

been been

great great

friend friend

different different

Spelling & Word Work

Word Cards: Words with *ee*

 wheel	 sweet	 bee	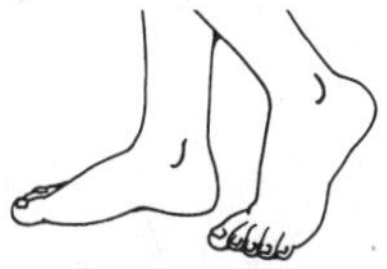 feet
she	deeds	he	sweeping
be	eve	agree	feed
beet	we	glee	tree
feel	flee	remix	these
extreme	delete	three	complete
theme	athlete	keep	green

High Frequency Word Cards

put	house
give	kind
does	place
away	both
before	been
after	great
through	friend
carry	different

Name ________________________ Date ______________

Comparison Chart

Compare Settings and Plots

Use this comparison chart to compare the settings and plots of the two fables by Aesop.

Title	Setting	Plot
"The Lion and the Mouse"	takes place in the forest	
"The Farmer and the Eagle"		

Share your comparison chart with a partner to talk about the fables.

Name ______________________________ Date ______________

Phonics

Words with *ea*

Use paper fasteners and paper clips to make two spinners. Spin them both and use the letters to make words below. If the letters don't make a word, spin again.

Make Spinners

1. Push a brad through the center of the spinner.
2. Open the brad on the back.
3. Hook a paper clip over the brad on the front to make a spinner.

Beginning of word

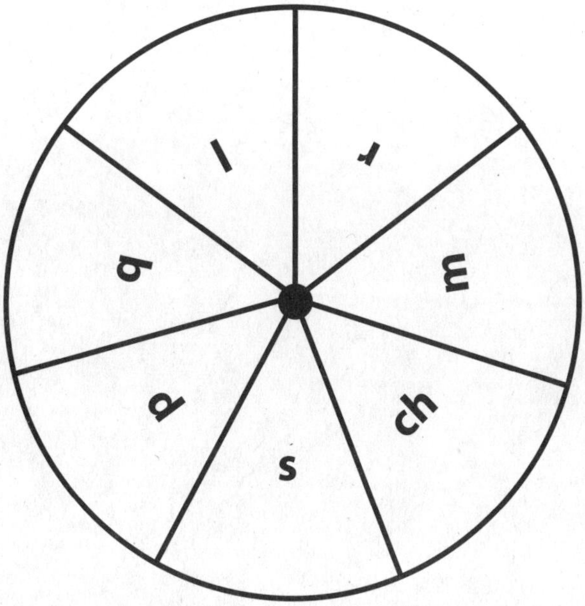

End of word

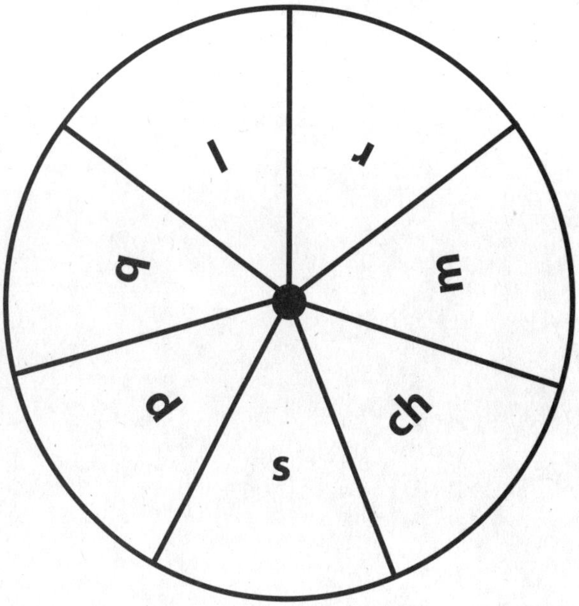

1. chief
2. beak
3. ie
4. ea
5. ea
6. ea
7. ea
8. ea
9. ea
10. ea
11. ea
12. ea

Name ________________________ Date ____________

High Frequency Words

Where Do You Live?

Write a word from the box to complete each sentence.

High Frequency **Words**
been
both
different
friend
great
house
kind
place

1. Lee is my best ________.

2. We ________ live on the same street.

3. My house is ________ from Lee's house.

4. My ________ of house has three homes in it.

5. Have you ________ to my street?

6. It is a great ________ to live!

Name ______________________________ Date ______________

Grammar: Word Order

Mix and Match Sentences

Choose words from each column and add any other words you need to make a statement. You may use words more than once.

Naming Part	Verb	Object
Mr. Yi	traded	fish
Mrs. Yi	caught	rice
Mr. Jia	shook	soup
They	dropped	bowl of rice
We	made	each other
I	paid	him
She	helped	it

Name ______________________ Date __________

Phonics

Words with *ea, ie*

Write the words to complete each sentence.

1. beach daydream

Kim and Jess sit and __________ at the __________.

2. sea brief

Then they go for a __________ swim in the __________.

3. relief heat

It is a __________ to get out of the __________.

4. seaweed real

Kim and Jess find __________ seashells and __________ in the sand.

5. eat peach

Then they get a __________ and some peanuts to

__________.

6. seagull steals

A __________ dives down and __________ some peanuts!

7. sneaks beak

It grabs them with its __________ and __________ away.

8. thief scream

Kim and Jess __________, "Stop that __________!"

Name ______________________ Date ______________

Grammar and Writing

Write Sentences

Unscramble the words to make a correct sentence. Write the sentence. Use a period.

1. need / help / I / with my homework / .

I need help with my homework.

2. helps / My brother / me / with science / .

____

3. thank / my brother / I / .

____

4. help / my brother / I / with the dishes / .

____

5. each other / We / help / .

____

Name ______________________ Date ____________

Grammar: Complete Sentence

Use Sentences

1. Play with a partner.
2. Toss a coin onto one of the sentence parts below.
3. Put it together with another sentence part to make a complete sentence.
4. Your partner takes a turn.
5. The player who makes the most complete sentences wins.

My friends	make good choices.
are thoughtful.	The teachers
My classmates	give to others.
help me study.	Mom and Dad
Our cousins	show respect.

Name ______________________ Date ____________

Phonics

Words with *oa, ow*

Circle the word that names the picture.

1.  row ray rob	**2.**  cot coat kite	**3.**  bell bone bowl
4.  crow cream crop	**5.**  rod road raid	**6.** 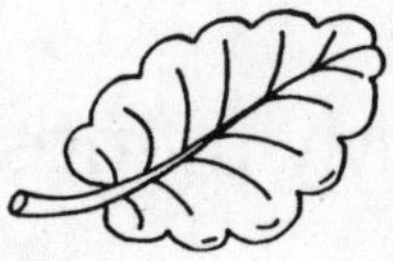 loaf loft leaf
7. 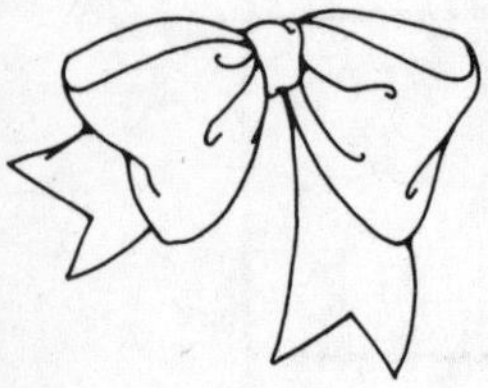 bay bow bee	**8.**  got gate goat	**9.** 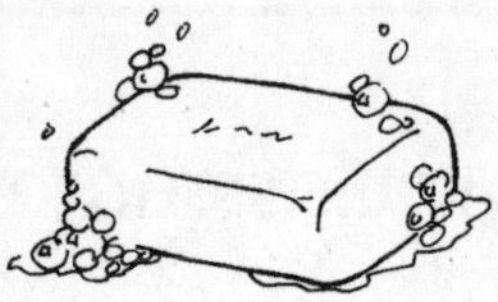 soap seep sip
10.  snail snow snob	**11.** 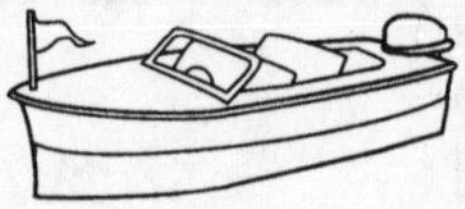 boat bait beat	**12.** 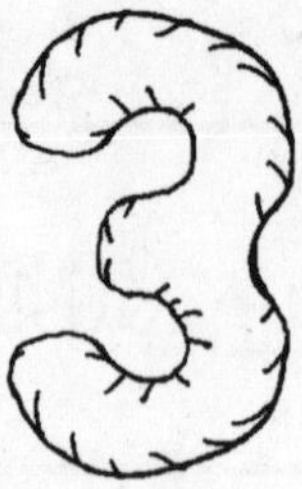 throne three throw

Read It Together I see a goat and a crow on the road.

Name ______________________ Date ______________

Sequence Chain

Sequence

Fill out the sequence chain to show events in order.

First	Next	Then	Finally

Use the sequence chain to tell the story to a partner.

Name ______________________ Date ______________

Phonics

Words with *oa, ow*

Write the words to complete each sentence. Then write what it is.

1. window yellow

It's ________, and it shines in my ________. ________

2. grows mow

It ________ fast, so I ________ it. ________

3. bowl oatmeal

It's what I do with the ________ in my ________. ________

4. coat snows

It's why I put on my ________ when it ________. ________

5. row boat

It's a ________ that I like to ________. ________

6. soaks rainbow

It ________ me before I see a ________. ________

7. toast loaf

It comes in a ________, and I can ________ it. ________

8. home throw

I can ________ it over ________ plate for you to hit!

____

Name ____________________ Date __________

Handwriting

High Frequency Words

Trace each High Frequency Word and then write it.

may may

ever ever

nice nice

thank thank

push push

around around

teacher teacher

would would

Spelling & Word Work

Word Cards: Words with *oa, ow*

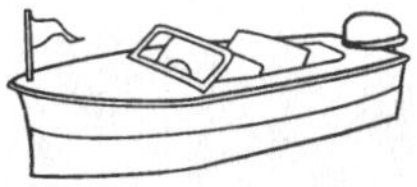 boat	 toad	 window	 elbow
bow	floating	toasted	swallow
throw	throat	mow	coast
moaning	narrow	goat	borrow
road	tow	groan	roadside
grow	row	steam-boat	below
moat	low	load	slow

Spelling & Word Work

High Frequency Word Cards

off	may
going	ever
clean	nice
stop	thank
think	push
our	around
let	teacher
take	would

Name ______________________ Date ____________

Phonics

More Words with Long *o*

Complete the word to name the picture.

1. 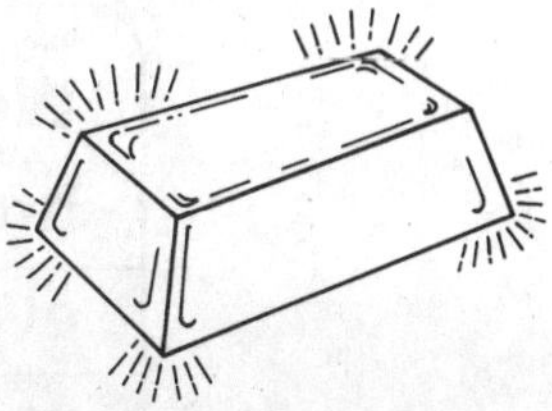 gold	**2.**  b lt
3.  c	**4.**  c lt
5.  h	**6.** 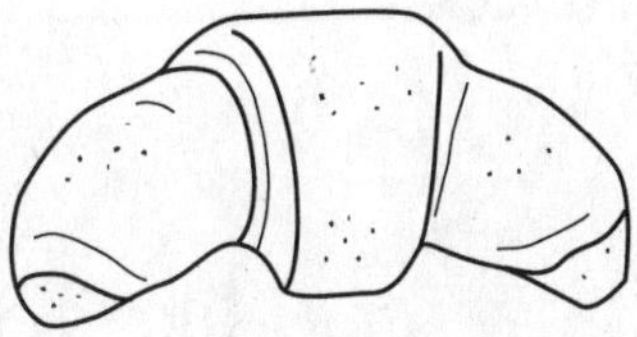 r ll

Read It Together Can you hold a colt?

Name ______________________________ Date ______________

High Frequency Words

Miss Gold

Write a word from the box to complete each sentence.

High Frequency **Words**
around
ever
may
nice
push
teacher
thank
would

1. Miss Gold is a very nice ________.

2. She may be the best one I've ________ had!

3. I want to ________ her for being so nice.

4. ________ you like to see our class?

5. You can ________ open the door and come in.

6. Look ________. See what makes Miss Gold so nice!

Grammar: Subjects and Predicates

Word Cards: Subjects and Predicates

the mountain	our hotel	you and I	those photographs
they	most people	a doctor	Alex and Connor
the mayor	her neighbors	children	sheep and cows
help	see	ask	want
hear	eat	visit	make
give	clean up	carry	show
remember	live	play	take

Name ______________________ Date ____________

Phonics

More Words with Long *o*

Write the word that completes each sentence.

1. **folding strolling**

   Jo is __________ down the path with her dog.

2. **gold elbow**

   Her dog looks __________ in the sunshine.

3. **window old**

   They pass an __________ gate.

4. **grow colt**

   A little __________ is with a man in the field.

5. **holding soaps**

   Jo is __________ her dog's leash.

6. **scold both**

   She uses __________ hands!

7. **don't fold**

   "I __________ want you to run through the gate and play!" she exclaims.

8. **strolling told**

   Now Jo and her dog are __________ back home.

9. **rolling cold**

   Jo is __________, so she wants some hot tea to drink.

Name ______________________ Date ____________

Grammar and Writing

Write Subjects and Verbs

Read the story. Then choose a word or words from the box that go with each sentence. Write the word.

the flyer	feel good because I helped a lot of people
our home	sometimes have trouble getting to the grocery store
I	walked around on different floors

Our home is in a big apartment building. I decided to help some older people in my building. They ______________________.

My dad and I ______________________. ______ passed out a flyer with my name and phone number on it. ________ said to call me and I would go to the grocery store for them. Many neighbors used my service. I ______________________.

Name ____________________ Date ____________

Sequence Chain

Giving Back

Fill out the sequence chain to show the order of events in "Giving Back."

First	Next	Then	Finally
William Allard sees a boy crying because his sheep have died.			

Tell a partner about the events in sequence.

Name ______________________________ Date ______________

Phonics

Compound Words

Connect the words to name the picture and write the compound word.

1. 

cup
tea ·········· pot

teapot

2. 

pack
back
seat

____

3. 

coat
rain
bow

____

4. 

robe
bath
tub

____

5. 

screen
sun
rise

____

6. 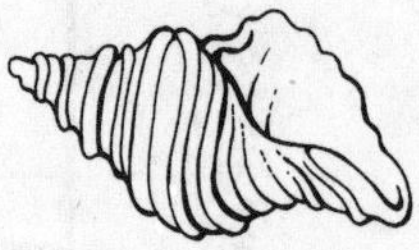

coast
sea
shell

____

7. 

cap
snow
flake

____

8. 

shake
hand
bag

____

9. 

dream
day
time

____

Read It Together I look for seashells on the seacoast at sunrise.

Name ______________________________ Date ______________

Phonics

Compound Words

Divide the syllables. Write the word that completes each sentence.

1. sunshine   treetop

The __________ was streaming in through the window.

2. peanut   backpack

Craig got his __________ and helmet to go for a bike ride.

3. homemade   outside

He went __________, but the day was gray.

4. raindrops   weekdays

Then some __________ fell on his nose.

5. daydream   inside

Craig went back __________.

6. beehive   raincoat

He put on his __________ and boots to go out and splash in the rain.

7. sailboat   snowflake

He went out, but a __________ fell on his nose!

8. into   maybe

Craig went back __________ the house for his hat and mittens.

9. snowman   bedside

Now he will go out to make a __________!

Name ______________________ Date ______________

Handwriting

High Frequency Words

Trace each High Frequency Word and then write it.

yes yes

say say

says says

write write

dear dear

name name

letter letter

answer answer

Spelling & Word Work

Word Cards: Compound Words

 newspaper	 eyebrow	 goldfish	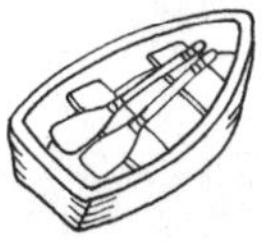 rowboat
teammate	grownup	walking	blueberry
diagram	sandbox	ladybug	thermometer
watermelon	never	wheelchair	seldom
seaside	cookbook	scarecrow	table
dining	butterfly	sunshine	paper
campfire	tattoo	towels	footprint

High Frequency Word Cards

land	yes
wash	say
city	write
much	dear
river	name
hold	letter
sea	says
mile	answer

Name ______________________ Date ____________

Comparison Chart

Compare Author's Purpose

Work with a partner to fill in the comparison chart.

Author's Purpose	William Allard	Carol Jordan and Arwa Damon
to persuade		
to inform		✓
to entertain		
to share experiences	✓	
to tell about other parts of the world		

Which selection did you like best? Share your opinion with a partner.

Name ______________________ Date ____________

Phonics

Abbreviations

Cut out the cards and mix them up. Match the words to the abbreviations and use them in sentences.

Mister	**Mr.**
Doctor	**Dr.**
Street	**St.**
Road	**Rd.**
Sunday	**Sun.**
April	**Apr.**

Name ________________________________ Date ______________

High Frequency Words

Mittens

Write a word from the box to complete each sentence.

High Frequency **Words**
answer
dear
letter
name
say
says
write
yes

________ Gramps,

We got a kitten! Her ________ is Mittens. When I say "Mittens," she has an ________ for me. She ________, "Mee-oo."

May Mittens and I visit you? I hope you say, "________!" Will you ________ me a letter? Tell me if we may visit.

Your grandson,

Jake

Word Cards: Subject-Verb Agreement

the boys	our house	Shannon and I	those CDs
they	you	the newspaper	my friends
the pilot	some players	a child	a dog
wait	says	run	makes
jump	eats	talks	think
chooses	tell	drives	hope
hear	takes	watches	gets

Name ______________________ Date ____________

Phonics

Abbreviations

Monday → Mon.
Mark Joseph Smith → M. J. Smith

Write the word that completes each sentence.

1. Mrs. St.

My mom is a teacher. Kids call her ________ Chan.

2. Wed. Mr.

My dad is a teacher, too. He is ________ Chan.

3. Dr. Rd.

Mom's class is going on a field trip to see a vet. The vet is ________ Gray.

4. St. Sun.

The kids get on the bus at 27 Pine ________ at 10 a.m.

5. Oct. Rd.

They get off the bus at 9 Hancock ________ at 10:30.

6. Nov. Ms.

They see the date Friday, ________10 on the vet's door.

7. Mon. P. C.

The vet shows them Mr. ________ Mason's cat.

8. Ave. Feb.

Mr. Mason and his cat live on Prescott ________ next to me!

Name ______________________________ Date ______________

Grammar and Writing

Write Verbs That Agree

Read the story. Then choose a word from the box that correctly completes each sentence. Decide if you need to add *s* or *es* to the verb.

feel	help	relax	take	wash	work

My mom is a hero to me. She works at a hard job to support my brother and me. Sometimes she ________ very tired after work and does not feel like playing with us or fixing dinner. Then my brother and I ________ as much as we can. We ________ the dishes. My brother ________ out the trash. Finally, my mom, my brother, and I all ________ .

Name ______________________________ Date ______________

Grammar: Subject-Verb Agreement

Use Subject-Verb Agreement

Grammar Rules Subject-Verb Agreement

Every sentence has two parts: the subject and the verb. The subject and verb must agree.

The boy waits. (one person)

Parents smile. (more than one person)

1. **Partner 1 points to a subject card.**
2. **Partner 2 points to a verb card.**
3. **If the subject and verb agree, cross out both cards.**
4. **Play until all the cards are crossed out.**

Subject Cards			
Avi	Teresa	Mr. and Mrs. Mendez	You and I
He	She	They	We

Verb Cards			
wants	builds	helps	hopes
work	study	need	carry